THE VALLEY IS BURNING

WHEN COMMUNICATIONS BECOMES THE CRISIS

Sarah Barczyk

The Valley Is Burning: When Communications Becomes the Crisis
by Sarah Barczyk

© Copyright 2023 Sarah Barczyk

ISBN
979-8-9883084-0-9—Hardcover
979-8-9883084-1-6—Paperback
979-8-9883084-2-3—Digital/E-Book

Dedicated in memory of Leonel Rondon and in honor of the resiliency of the affected residents of Lawrence, Andover and North Andover. May we always remember and continue to learn and improve.

In memory of Mike Davidson (March 9, 1962-September 27, 2022) You left this world a better place for having been in it, and that's all any of us can ever hope for.

CONTENTS

FOREWORD

was just leaving a reception on Capitol Hill when the phone rang. I had testified to Congress in that same hearing room earlier that day, but this evening, the hearing room was being used for a reception to honor my new colleague on the National Transportation Safety Board (NTSB).

On the other end of the phone was NTSB's managing director, Sharon Bryson. "Hate to bother you, Chairman, but there's been an apparent natural gas explosion outside of Boston. It looks serious. Can you come to the office?"

Twenty minutes later, I joined others in my conference room at NTSB headquarters. CNN was switching back and forth between the pending arrival of Hurricane Florence, which was due to hit the Carolinas within hours, and this developing story. The Massachusetts towns of Lawrence, Andover, and North Andover were experiencing multiple fires. Much of the entire town of Lawrence was evacuated, along with several neighborhoods in Andover and North Andover. Numerous homes were on fire and destroyed. Tragically, the life of 18-year-old Leonel Rondon was lost when a house he was visiting exploded. Media sources were reporting that an overpressure of the natural gas system was behind these massive and seemingly random explosions and fires. This was soon confirmed to us by the Department of Transportation's pipeline division, Pipeline and Hazardous Materials Safety Administration (PHMSA).

Known best for investigating aviation accidents, it may be surprising to many that NTSB also investigates pipeline accidents, including those involving natural gas. Therefore, this accident would be squarely within NTSB's jurisdiction; we would send a Go Team to begin the investigation. The next morning, 12 of us boarded a government jet, bound for the Merrimack Valley of Massachusetts.

The command post for all the federal, state, and local agencies involved in managing the disaster was set up in the large parking lot of a shopping center in Lawrence. Otherwise, the city was like a ghost town. There was no electricity in the entire area. All streets were blocked off. Businesses were shuttered. I recall seeing a gas station where the door of a truck was left wide open at the gas pumps. It was surreal. People stopped in the middle of whatever they were doing and fled.

While the investigative staff began doing what they do best, my job was to conduct media interviews and meet with elected officials, including Massachusetts Senator Ed Markey and then-Governor Charlie Baker. Of course, there were many more questions than answers, but in the ensuing days, we could at least answer why the over-pressurization occurred. The owner and operator of the pipeline system, Columbia Gas of Massachusetts, whose parent company was NiSource, had overlooked a critical step when planning construction to replace older pipe in Lawrence[1]. While contractors were cutting-in the new pipe, the company's planning error manifested

---

1   NTSB's Final Accident Report on the Merrimack Valley accident, NTSB/PAR-19-02 PB2019-101365, can be found by visiting: https://www.ntsb.gov/investigations/AccidentReports/Reports/PAR1902.pdf

itself; high pressure gas was allowed to enter gas distribution lines that were designed for much lower pressure. Homes that weren't designed to withstand such higher pressures caught fire.

Having fulfilled my duties of meeting with elected officials and holding two media briefings to explain the NTSB's investigative process, and to shed light on the immediate cause of the fires and explosions, my job here was finished; it was time for me to head back to Washington, DC. While the NTSB investigation team would be on scene for several more days and weeks, future investigative information would be released by NTSB media relations officials in Washington.

A few days after I left Merrimack Valley, a bright and skillful communications expert, NiSource's Sarah Barczyk, arrived to lead the company's public relations and media efforts. Contrasting my role to Sarah's, I was there for only three days; Sarah was boots on ground for months. My job was relatively easy - NTSB was seen as the honest broker, called in to conduct an independent and competent investigation. NiSource and Columbia Gas of Mass, on the other hand, were immediately looked upon as the responsible party. These companies were squarely in the crosshairs of criticism from displaced residents, the public at large, politicians, media, and state and federal regulatory officials.

Now that NTSB had provided a plausible explanation for the explosions and fires, the focus of the local community turned to one of immediate concern: how long before they could return to their homes? As discussed in *The Valley is Burning: When Communications Becomes the Crisis,* the answers to those questions were complicated. In this book, Sarah doesn't sugarcoat the situation. There were problems, disappointments, and setbacks.

Within the pages of this book, Sarah provides her real-world experiences of managing communications and public relations during this crisis. She's been there and done it, and she did so under extremely difficult circumstances. Her credibility and experience set her apart from others.

As I read the manuscript, I couldn't help writing supportive comments in the margins to denote my wholehearted agreement with her points. Not only is this book an interesting read, but it is also chock-full of lessons learned about managing a crisis. Sarah Barczyk provides many useful tips that, if properly used, will help a communications practitioner avoid making the same mistakes. To make these points easy to refer to, Sarah included an appendix that pulls together all the recommendations into one section.

There's a saying, "Learn from the mistakes of others. You won't live long enough to make them all yourself." As NTSB on-scene spokesperson for 35 accidents, and for several others that I didn't travel to, I, myself, made plenty of mistakes. Looking back, I wish I had the benefit of Sarah's knowledge and experience before stepping into my NTSB communications role.

The way you handle a crisis can either make you or break you. The tools outlined in *The Valley is Burning: When Communications Becomes the Crisis* will strengthen your abilities to survive. Wishing you great success as you navigate your organization's crises.

Robert L. Sumwalt
NTSB Board Member, 2006 – 2021
NTSB Chairman, 2017-2021
Ormond Beach, FL
May 2023

INTRODUCTION

On September 13, 2018, a series of natural gas explosions in Massachusetts shook the Merrimack Valley, just north of Boston, to its very core. Residents of the towns of Andover and North Andover, as well as the city of Lawrence, would be directly affected for the next several months. Twenty-one people were injured and one person—an 18-year-old man named Leonel Rondon—was killed as a result of the explosions.

Following the initial explosions, the longer-term response to the pipeline accident, which compromised the pipeline system as well as homes, businesses and their natural gas appliances, was difficult, lengthy and more complex than could have been initially imagined. Reaction to the accident prompted a massive response from NiSource and its responsible subsidiary, Columbia Gas of Massachusetts, as well as the federal and local governments, the natural gas and energy industry, and scores of first responders. None of the entities involved were prepared for the ensuing response efforts.

Hundreds of employees from NiSource and its Columbia Gas subsidiary companies in Pennsylvania, Maryland, Ohio, Virginia, Kentucky and Indiana were deployed to the Merrimack Valley to aid in the restoration and recovery effort. Contractors and consultants from every business discipline also spent time on the ground in Massachusetts and remotely in an attempt to repair the pipeline system and return affected residents to their homes with heat and hot water before the harsh northeastern winter bore down on the area.

The Valley is Burning—When Communications Becomes the Crisis offers a timeline of events from a communications perspective as observed by someone who was involved in the response effort in differing roles throughout the accident response. This account of the Merrimack Valley accident is not intended to expose any persons or organization, nor does it aim to place blame or cast suspicion. Each person who was involved in both the initial and extended restoration and recovery response from Columbia Gas and other NiSource companies, along with contract and consulting partners, devoted up to three months of their life (or more) to restore heat, hot water and peace of mind to affected residents of Lawrence, Andover and North Andover. Those employees, contractors and consultants missed significant family events and altered their lives greatly to respond to this emergency.

While *The Valley is Burning* does not deeply assess the cause of the incident, and instead discusses the communications response effort, I highly recommend readers familiarize themselves with the NTSB Accident Report: *Overpressurization of Natural Gas Distribution System, Explosions, and Fires in Merrimack Valley Massachusetts,*[2] along with accompanying documents that describe the events leading up to the accident. A series of seemingly small missteps and inconsequential timing issues contributed to the explosions and multiple fires that required the massive recovery operation.

What happened in September of 2018 was an unprecedented event in the natural gas industry that triggered one of the largest deployments of on-the-ground emergency response resources in recent years, outside of natural

---

2   NTSB/PAR-19/02 PB2019-101365, adopted September 24, 2019. https://ntsb.gov/
     investigations/AccidentReports/Reports/PAR1902.pdf

disaster response. As Chief Recovery Officer Joseph Albanese reportedly said, "It was like building the fire engine on the way to the fire."[3] Could we, as a company, industry, and as communicators, have done things differently? Yes. Could we have done things better? Without a doubt. But this was the first experience of its kind for responders, and the team was learning day-by-day. My hope is for this book to be used as a guide for crisis communicators and those interested in crisis communications response so they might take away some lessons from someone who had to learn those lessons firsthand.

The book is structured chronologically and is written from my perspective alone. Each chapter discusses a different phase in the process, either as it had been officially reported, or as I experienced it. Anything presented that is not from my personal experience or perspective has been researched and cited accordingly. I have endeavored not to speculate regarding situations I was not a part of, and I've taken care to avoid making assumptions. Each chapter ends with takeaways or "lessons learned" from my experience. Those who lived through this event with me may recognize their (paraphrased) words or the part they played, but I have called out very few people by name, though they may be identified in referenced and cited materials.

I am not acting as a representative or spokesperson for NiSource or Columbia Gas in any capacity in the writing of this text or the relaying of this information. All views and opinions are strictly my own, based on my own experiences.

---

3   Bergstein, Brian. "It was a Suburban Disaster," https://www.bu.edu/articles/2019/merrimack-valley-gas-explosions-joe-albanese/. Bostonia, 2019.

CHAPTER 1

THE EVENT— A BRIEF OVERVIEW

During the summer of 2018, Columbia Gas of Massachusetts (CMA), at the time a NiSource subsidiary natural gas distribution company, was working on a number of large-scale pipeline replacement projects throughout the Commonwealth of Massachusetts. The effort to replace aged pipeline had been going on for approximately a decade. The pipeline replacement work involved replacing cast iron and bare steel pipeline with state-of-the-art polyethylene plastic pipeline meant to last well into future generations. Similar work had been undertaken by many natural gas utilities across the nation as part of a commitment to replace aging infrastructure and enhance public safety.[4]

---

4   This replacement work (and all operations of natural gas distribution systems) across the United States involves oversight from state regulatory commissions. In Massachusetts, this entity is known as the Department of Public Utilities (DPU).

1

The following overview of the incident on September 13, 2018, is paraphrased from the National Transportation Safety Board (NTSB) Accident Report, titled *Overpressurization of Natural Gas Distribution System, Explosions, and Fires in Merrimack Valley*, Massachusetts September 13, 2018. This report was published on September 24, 2019.[5]

On September 13, 2018, an employee of CMA's construction organization and four subcontracted natural gas construction employees were working on an ongoing pipeline replacement project at the corner of Salem and South Union Streets in Lawrence, Massachusetts. As part of the work, this construction crew was replacing the existing cast iron mainline with a plastic polyethylene mainline on a low-pressure natural gas distribution system.[6] Work on this project had begun two years earlier in 2016 but had been delayed due to city restrictions and street paving in the area.

The work taking place in September 2018 in the city of Lawrence involved connecting the previously installed polyethylene line to the overall natural gas distribution system including a regulator station[7] and abandoning (or fully disconnecting) the existing cast iron pipeline. This is routine work and is performed as a part of pipeline replacement projects on a regular basis.

Unfortunately, during the replacement work happening in Lawrence, the sensing lines, which allow the pipeline pressure regulators[8] to detect the amount of pressure in the natural gas system, had not been reconnected to

---

5   https://www.ntsb.gov/investigations/AccidentReports/Reports/PAR1902.pdf

6   The distribution system is the series of pipelines that feed homes and businesses.

7   A small facility that measures and regulates the pressure of the flow of natural gas through the system.

8   As natural gas moves through a system, pressure regulators control the flow of gas from higher to lower pressures. If a regulator senses that the pressure has dropped below a certain point, the regulator will open to allow more gas to flow. If the pressure is measured above a certain point, the regulator will close to adjust the flow of gas accordingly.

the new and active polyethylene mainline. Instead, they were still connected to the old cast iron main when it was abandoned and disconnected from service. The regulators detected dropping pressure in the abandoned cast iron pipeline to which the sensing lines were still connected. As the pressure dropped, the pressure regulators responded to the apparent loss of pressure and opened further, increasing pressure in the active and newly connected natural gas distribution system and releasing high-pressure natural gas into the low-pressure system. For comparison's sake, this would be like hooking up a garden hose to the heavy flow and pressure of the water coming out of a fire hydrant.

As the high-pressure natural gas coursed through the low-pressure system in the residential area and communities of Lawrence, Andover and North Andover, it flowed with enough force to blow out the standard regulator devices installed on natural gas appliances inside homes. The force of the gas overwhelmed the system, and at approximately 4:00 p.m. on September 13, a series of explosions began, causing multiple fires, as the gas entered homes through natural gas appliances and ignited.

The explosions caused by the system overpressurization damaged over 100 structures, and several homes and businesses were destroyed by the explosions. Eighteen-year-old Leonel Rondon was killed. He was sitting in a car on the driveway of a house when the chimney collapsed following an explosion, falling on and crushing the vehicle. At least 23 people, including first responders, were sent to hospitals around the area.

Fire departments and first responders from Lawrence, Andover and North Andover rushed toward the chaotic scene with no idea to what they were responding. The cause of the incident was not immediately known, and there were even initial reports of potential malfeasance or terrorism. According to the NTSB Accident Report, first responders initiated their fire mobilization plan and received mutual aid from nearby locations in Massachusetts, New Hampshire and Maine. The first responders closed local roads and ceased all rail transportation in the area, and the local electricity provider shut down power in the area. Less than an hour after the first emergency calls were received, the Massachusetts Emergency Management Agency (MEMA) activated the Fire Mobilization plan, engaging 15 task forces across the state, and over 180 fire department and 140 law enforcement agencies responded to the scene.

Within 90 minutes of the first explosions, evacuation orders were issued to the residents of the three municipalities, using text alerts, media broadcasts, local cable channels, town websites and citizen alert telephone systems.

It took over 14 hours[9] for Columbia Gas to shut down and completely lock in the low-pressure system, which then shut off the gas service of over 10,000 customers, some of whom were outside of the immediately impacted area. For those customers not affected by the overpressurization, their service was shut off merely as a safety precaution.

In total, over 50,000 residents in the Merrimack Valley were ordered to evacuate, and five dedicated locations were set up in the three communities to help to serve residents who had been displaced by the incident. These locations offered gift cards, information and resources for people who had nowhere else to turn. Some of these centers became overnight shelters and remained open for days. While residents were allowed to return to their homes in all three municipalities on September 16, many homes were uninhabitable, and without gas service for heating, hot water and cooking, the homes remained uninhabitable for several months following the initial explosions.

During this time a number of events took place that required considerable integration internally and with external agencies, the implementation of new and enhanced processes, response efforts to affected residents and

---

9 All of the regulator stations were shut within four hours. It took fourteen hours to confirm that the system was completely locked in and secure.

governing bodies and emergent situations that required agility and flexibility. Every situation that occurred required extensive communications efforts.

As previously mentioned, *The Valley is Burning* will address the communications effort surrounding the overpressurization event and the following restoration and recovery work. If you are interested in a more in-depth explanation of the events leading up to the explosions, I encourage you to review the NTSB Accident Report. An additional resource dealing mainly with the response and recovery efforts from a state perspective was issued by the Massachusetts Emergency Management Agency (MEMA). This document, titled *Merrimack Valley Gas Explosions After Action Report: September 13-December 16, 2018*[10], was published in January 2020.

---

10   https://www.mass.gov/doc/merrimack-valley-natural-gas-explosions-after-action-report/download

CHAPTER 2

THE FIRST FIVE HOURS

On the afternoon of September 13, 2018, I held the position of director of communications for a Columbia Gas subsidiary company in Pennsylvania, under the holding company NiSource. In this position as a company leader, I routinely provided communication support in the incidents of natural gas leaks, large-scale natural gas outages, and third-party damages related to gas lines that may have been hit or compromised during routine pipeline or other construction work. These types of events often resulted in situations that caused concern for customers' health and safety. Especially in the winter months, natural gas outages became a much larger issue when customers were left without heat and/or hot water.

Our communications team frequently interfaced with the local media, and communicated with customers, the public and other external stakeholders through social media channels, website updates, customer emails, texts and phone calls, while also serving as the clearing house for any information related to an outage or an incident, both internally and externally. The safety and well-being of our customers, contractors and employees, were top of mind in every emergency situation in which we were involved.

On that fateful day in September, I had arrived home at 5:00 pm EDT, and was preparing to go out to dinner when I received a text from a friend and colleague.

Something bad is happening in Massachusetts.

I knew this message was referring to our sister subsidiary of Columbia Gas of Massachusetts (CMA), and immediately searched the internet for coverage. I was shocked by what I viewed online. Towns in Massachusetts were literally burning, and initial reports indicated that natural gas explosions were to blame for the devastation.[11] CMA was being named as the natural gas provider in the area.

Flames consume the roof of a home following an explosion in Lawrence, Mass., September 13, 2018.
Photo credit: AP File Photo, Editorial License

---

11 While news reports had preliminarily speculated on natural gas explosions as the cause of the incident in the Merrimack Valley, NiSource and Columbia Gas of Massachusetts did not confirm these reports and worked with investigators at the National Transportation and Safety Board (NTSB) before a cause was stated publicly.

My first call was to the president of my subsidiary company in Pennsylvania. He was unaware of the incident and as shocked as I had been by his initial scan of the coverage. We disconnected quickly so he could track down information. I visited the CMA Facebook page. Nothing had been posted. On the CMA Twitter feed, no updates had been shared.

Graphic coverage of burning homes and devastation continued to be displayed on the major national news networks and other Massachusetts outlets, all reporting multiple explosions and fires due to a natural gas incident in an area known as the Merrimack Valley.[12]

I called my corporate communications counterpart at NiSource headquarters, and my call was sent straight to voicemail. I then sent texts to multiple communications peers throughout the company. I finally received a response from another counterpart on the corporate communications team who shared the response: *This is bad.*

Do we know what's happening?

We're still trying to get details.

Do we have a statement?

Nothing has been approved yet.

Not wanting to disturb my CMA colleagues, but wanting to do something— whatever I could—to help, I texted the director of communications for CMA.

Are you okay? Is there anything I can do?

My counterpart responded immediately with one word: *Pray.*

I did pray, but I wanted to do something else. I wanted to respond. I wanted to get out in front of those cameras that were now filming firefighters and first responders, showing the charred remains of homes and businesses that were still actively burning, and featuring displaced customers and piles of rubble. I wanted to say something. I wanted to say *anything.*

---

12   The Merrimack Valley is made up of the cities, towns and communities along the Merrimack River in New Hampshire and Massachusetts.

Looking back, saying anything, even if it had been a simple, "We have crews on the ground, and we're assessing the situation," would have been infinitely more effective than what we did. Which was to remain silent and wait.

Of course, there were reasons for waiting. And at the time, without having any details regarding cause and without receiving good intelligence about the chaotic situation on the ground, plunging forward with a statement, even a benign one, would have been a difficult decision.

In the meantime, the president of my subsidiary called me back and confirmed what we all knew— the situation *appeared* to be the result of a gas-related incident, though it was still much too soon to speculate on cause. The limited information coming out of Massachusetts was understandable, but it was also frightening, and our team in Pennsylvania felt helpless.

I ended up going to dinner, because there was nothing more I could do at that point. But I couldn't stop looking at my phone. I distinctly remember the words of my significant other, also a communicator: "I don't know why you keep looking at your phone. This isn't your problem."

Those words would come back to haunt us.

Five hours after the incident had first been reported, CMA issued a statement[13] to the press and the public via its website. To paraphrase, the statement confirmed that natural gas crews were responding to reports of multiple fires in Lawrence and offered thoughts and acknowledgement for everyone affected by the situation. CMA also thanked local emergency responders for their actions and outlined steps customers should take upon detecting an odor of natural gas.

---

13   "Columbia Gas issues statement following explosions in Lawrence, Andover and North Andover." Bombard, Noah R., https://www.masslive.com/news/boston/2018/09/columbia_gas_issues_statement.html. September 14, 2018.

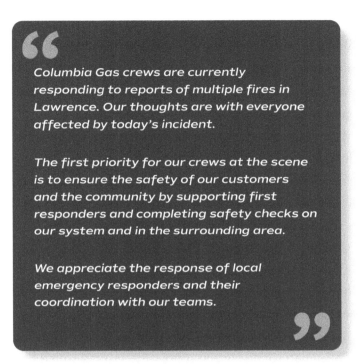

> *Columbia Gas crews are currently responding to reports of multiple fires in Lawrence. Our thoughts are with everyone affected by today's incident.*
>
> *The first priority for our crews at the scene is to ensure the safety of our customers and the community by supporting first responders and completing safety checks on our system and in the surrounding area.*
>
> *We appreciate the response of local emergency responders and their coordination with our teams.*

If that statement had been issued within the first hour, or even within two hours of the incident, it may have been adequate. But five hours later, many customers, public officials and members of the media criticized this statement as being too little, too late.

In the five hours prior to this statement being posted, a young man died and 23 people were hospitalized. In those five hours, some residents in the affected areas lost everything they owned. In those five hours, lives shifted and changed forever.

You may be wondering why there was a delay in issuing the statement, which is fairly high-level and unremarkable. While I was not a part of that process, nor was I privy to the decision-making, I will reiterate that this was an unprecedented event in the natural gas industry. Because of the danger, widespread damage and subsequent traffic restrictions and emergency response, it took CMA employees much longer than normal to be able to assess the situation and make any sort of determination regarding the preliminary cause. There were also unknown liability issues to consider, as well as complex legal factors to be taken into consideration. Additionally, the executive team was largely in the air, en route to the scene, and unavailable to approve such an important public acknowledgement.

Many in the industry and in the field of communications firmly believe that if representatives from CMA had spoken out earlier, through any channel, the response may have smoothed the way for future interaction with public officials, the media, and the residents and customers in the communities affected by the accident.

While an earlier statement may not have changed the ultimate outcome of the situation, a prepared and trained presence on camera, accompanied by a timely statement on social media and the company website, may have calmed some anxious residents and the general public looking for reassurance. At the very least, the company may not have become the immediate target of an outrage that would continue to grow. It would have also given the company the ability to attempt to control the narrative. By delaying the response, the company allowed the story to be told by others and found itself in a reactive and defensive position.

KEY TAKEAWAYS
(Lessons Learned)

Be Prepared: No matter your industry, draft and obtain pre-approval for a series of holding statements for emergencies that may affect your company. While every situation is unique, many crises share common elements. The goal should not be to tell the whole story, but to say something quickly and take control of the situation and the narrative, even when the granular details aren't immediately available or able to be communicated. Your legal team may push back, but remind your counsel of the public relations impact of *not* responding. Yes, there will be situations where you won't want to reveal all the details for legal and privacy-related reasons, but that should never preclude you from addressing the situation directly in some capacity and telling your own story.

Establish Internal Relationships: Take the time to establish positive relationships with your legal team or legal representatives *before* a crisis hits and have a crisis communications discussion with your legal team. When dealing with a fast-moving, ever-changing crisis, precious time should not be spent trying to identify the appropriate legal contact. And during a crisis is not the time to establish initial contact with your counterparts in your law organization. As a communicator, you should be joined at the hip with your legal counsel as partners. These relationships will prove critical when you need timely approval of messaging in any type of emergency situation.

Name and Train Your Leaders: Identify your approved spokespeople—who will oftentimes be company executives—ahead of time, and ensure they are media trained. A good media trainer will advise that the media outlets, while wanting to break the story and gain as many viewers/readers/followers as possible, are not out to ruin companies or damage reputations. And in fact, in a crisis situation, the media can be a crucial channel to communicate information swiftly and efficiently to a large number of stakeholders. In a fast-moving and emotionally charged situation, consider the question, "How is this interaction going to help the people I'm trying to reach?" At a minimum, the affected parties usually want to know:

1. What is happening?
2. Am I, or is my family, in danger?
3. What (if anything) do I need to do?
4. Is there any additional information that is necessary for me to know at this time?
5. What happens next?

In general, this applies to all media interactions, even those that are unsolicited and do not involve a crisis or the public at large. Interaction with the media may not always be comfortable, but taking responsibility or simply saying, "We just don't know yet," can help to diffuse the situation until more concrete details can be gathered, confirmed, approved for public distribution and communicated publicly.

Be Ready to Act: At least one of your executive leadership team members should be able to mobilize quickly and be prepared to make an on-camera statement in the event of a large-scale crisis. For an executive, this is part of the job, lending credibility and gravitas to a serious situation. Keep in mind that the executive does not necessarily need to be the chief executive officer. It could be another member of the C-Suite who holds a position of authority and can represent the company or organization. Don't wait until the last minute to try to arrange media training for your executive team. Prioritize media training and readiness *before* a crisis occurs and remember to schedule yearly refresher training for your executives, your communications team and for yourself.

Understand Roles and Responsibilities: The role of the executive in front of the camera is different than the role of spokesperson in a large crisis situation where injuries, death and/or property damage has occurred. The purpose of a spokesperson is to deliver vital emerging information and any detail the public needs to know immediately. Sometimes, the purpose of the spokesperson may be to provide a simple holding statement attributed to either the spokesperson him- or herself, or to the company. Conversely, the role of the executive is to act as the face of the company—to be seen as its heart and soul. Sometimes an executive's role is to take responsibility for an event or to offer an apology. It's not easy, but it's what good leaders should be able to do. One of the jobs of a communications professional is to ensure that executives are aware of and prepared for this sometimes-difficult task.

Establish External Relationships: Prior to a crisis, take some time to get to know your local media contacts by promoting stories of good will, if possible. Being a good corporate citizen is typically a goal of any organization, and promoting those efforts through the media can benefit the company beyond building a positive public image. Companies and careers are often built on relationships, and creating a respectful and mutually beneficial relationship with local media reporters and personalities can lend to your credibility as a company, especially if those relationships are founded on philanthropy or customer/community service. Having a friendly public face on your side in any situation can help to lend empathy and credibility to your cause.

Clarify Responsibility for Crisis Communications *Before* a Crisis: In companies with corporate communications departments as well as division communications teams, don't wait until an emergency to understand who is responsible for the communications function. The division of responsibility for functions, communications and beyond, should be understood well in advance of an accident scenario. If you're trying to determine whose job it is to perform what function in the midst of a crisis, at best, you will lose precious time. At worse, this indecisiveness may inadvertently exacerbate the situation.

Be Mindful of What's Important: At the end of the day, a company's reputation is built on how it treats its employees, its customers/stakeholders and the respect it shows the general public. Without a good reputation, bolstered by mindful public relations efforts, few companies survive in the long term.

overpressurization event. The NTSB's involvement and NiSource's status as a party to the investigation meant that every piece of communication produced by the company needed to be scrutinized to an even greater degree.

Two U.S. senators from Massachusetts, both extremely prominent public figures locally and nationally, arrived on the ground and toured the damaged areas, along with local elected officials. Both senators made statements criticizing CMA's communications efforts, among other areas of responsibility.[15]

Senator Ed Markey, D-MA, tours the damage in the Merrimack Valley with an NTSB investigator in September of 2018.
Photo credit: NTSB

Just before 4:00 pm EDT on September 14, the governor of Massachusetts and the mayor of the city of Lawrence held a press conference,[16] during which the governor declared a state of emergency in Lawrence, Andover and North Andover. The official declaration put the Massachusetts Department of Public

---

15 Copies of a letter to Columbia Gas demanding answers for the accident can be found here: https://www.markey.senate.gov/imo/media/doc/Letter%20to%20NiSource%20 and%20Columbia%20Gas.pdf.

16 Footage of this press conference can be found at: https://www.bostonmagazine.com/ news/2018/09/14/state-of-emergency-columbia-gas-fire-lawrence/ along with multiple news stories from September 14, 2018.

Utilities[17] (DPU) in charge of the recovery effort, and it was announced that a peer utility in Massachusetts had been tasked with completing the work necessary to allow residents return to their homes. Representatives from Columbia Gas were, notably, not participants in the press conference.

While both the governor and the mayor of Lawrence acknowledged the enormity of the event itself, the mayor was extremely critical of CMA's efforts and response. He continued to be a vocal detractor of the company throughout the recovery and restoration.

Those of us watching from afar had many questions. *What did it mean that the DPU was taking over the investigation? How would the restoration of service on the Columbia Gas system take place if another company who had no access to those systems was placed in charge of the restoration efforts?* Just as the event itself was unprecedented, so was this reaction by a state government.

Following the governor's press conference, during which CMA was criticized for its lack of response and lack of communication, the then president of CMA held his own brief press conference.[18] It marked the first time CMA publicly and directly addressed the residents of Lawrence, North Andover and Andover after the incident had occurred. On a personal note, I got the chance to know this man during my tenure with Columbia Gas, and he is one of the kindest and most genuine souls I have ever met. Even though the speaker was a good man, and despite the fact he was trying to do the right thing, the press conference was widely criticized. Two sentences were particularly troublesome:

We are sorry and deeply concerned about the inconvenience. This is the sort of thing that a gas distribution company hopes never happens.

---

17   https://www.mass.gov/orgs/department-of-public-utilities.

18   The press conference given by the then-president of CMA can be viewed in its entirety at https://www.facebook.com/watch/live/?v=329093114333088&ref=watch_permalink.

The word "inconvenience," was perceived as particularly troubling, given the fact a young man had been killed, nearly two dozen people had been injured, and homes had been destroyed.

Additionally, at this point in the crisis, evacuated residents were still displaced and did not have an estimated time of return. Residents continued to be traumatized by the accident and experienced elevated levels of stress and emotional trauma. Businesses had also been affected by the accident, meaning that livelihoods were at stake. This situation was much more than an inconvenience.

The second sentence—*This is the sort of thing that a gas distribution company hopes never happens*—seemed to make the tragedy about the company rather than the customers, who should have been top of mind. While the statement was well-intended, the perception was something else entirely. But between intent and perception, in the field of public relations, perception will always win.

Additionally, and optimistically, the president of CMA also told displaced customers he believed they would be able to return to their homes by Saturday (September 15) or Sunday (September 16). And while those residents may have been able to *return* to their homes in a few days, in fact, it would be many months until some of those customers would be able to *inhabit* their residences again.

The then CEO of NiSource also participated in a press conference the afternoon of September 14, 2018.[19] He expressed his sincere apologies along with a commitment to work with the NTSB, elected officials and customers, and acknowledged that the lack of public response in the first 24 hours had damaged confidence in the company's leadership. He pledged to partner

---

19   The NiSource CEO interview can be found at: https://www.boston25news.com/news/emergency-crews-responding-to-multiple-fires-following-explosions-in-lawrence/833085938/.

closely with the communities to provide residents and city and town leadership with whatever they needed. The tone was sincere and remorseful, but it came after a rough start.

KEY TAKEAWAYS
(Lessons Learned)

Review Your Messaging and Read for Intent: To the extent practical, communications professionals must partner with and guide executives in their public statements and ensure that every word is both written and delivered with the proper intent. In the case of the press conference given by the CMA president, the use of the word "inconvenience" was perceived as a lack of empathy for the family of the young man killed and for those injured in the incident. In its worst interpretation, the statement seemed self-centered in a situation during which injuries, death and trauma had occurred. The word "inconvenience" gave the impression the company was downplaying the problem during a time when people felt helpless, scared and angry.

Take Responsibility: An apology and an acknowledgement of responsibility goes a long way. In this instance, the statement, "This is the sort of thing a gas distribution company hopes never happens," in addition to shifting the focus to the company rather than on the customers, implies that safety is achieved not by skillful workers following rigorous policies and procedure, but rather by happenstance, which is not the case. With hindsight as an advantage, a better response may have been:

We deeply regret the events of September 13, and our thoughts are with everyone injured and affected by this tragic event. In particular, our thoughts are with the family of Leonel Rondon. While we cannot speculate on cause at this point, we commit to full compliance with the investigation and will provide investigators with any and all information needed to produce a final assessment of cause. In the meantime, we are working around the clock to get people back into their homes as quickly and safely as possible.

You are rightfully angry, unsure and upset. And we apologize. We pledge to do better and communicate with you honestly, transparently and in a timely fashion as we work with our partners in the public sector and with leaders of the municipalities to restore your service, and to restore your confidence.

Practice Makes Perfect: Similar to the Key Takeaways section of Chapter 2, it will be worthwhile for your company to consider worst-case scenarios, draft a statement of apology and practice this statement during media training. Remember, a statement such as this should be delivered by a company executive who holds a position of authority and can speak as a face of the company—not as the spokesperson, but as the embodiment of a corporate entity. While communicators may not be responsible for delivering this statement, they are responsible for the training and practice it takes to get the statement right. If you and your teams haven't held these conversations with your executives, the time to do so is now (not when a crisis occurs).

Trust but Verify: Ensure that you and your team have factual and confirmed information to share. The company didn't know it at the time, but many customers would not return to their homes for up to three months following the explosions. Some businesses closed permanently. The statement given during the CMA president's press conference indicated that customers could expect to have gas service restored to them within the next two days. While no one could have predicted the overwhelming obstacles to the restoration of gas service that would occur during the following weeks and months, reaction to the press conference serves as a reminder that only concrete information that has been confirmed by the proper subject matter experts should be shared.

Avoid sharing estimations or speculation, and be mindful of statements that could be misconstrued or misinterpreted. While it's tempting to deliver an optimistic pledge to restore trust and offer hope, if the information cannot be verified beyond doubt, avoid making promises that you may not be able to keep.

Understand Dependencies: Connections are key, both internally and externally. In addition to voices of elected officials from the three affected municipalities, by Friday morning, the Massachusetts governor, two U.S. senators and multiple state elected officials had joined together to criticize the company's communications and response efforts. It quickly became clear that working in an isolated manner was not a strong strategy.

Every part of the organization—executive leadership, operations, communications, government affairs, regulatory affairs, legal, information technology, supply chain, human resources, finance, etc.—is dependent upon other functions for accurate updates. The dispersion of that information, along with those connections, must take place internally in order to be able to share correct and timely information externally. As a communicator or a public information officer in a crisis, you may become the fulcrum of that information. It is important to understand that responsibility and take an active role in the distribution of messaging. Ask questions and push back if necessary. Your questioning attitude may make all the difference in the outcome of the situation.

It's All Connected: For all companies, it is imperative that the leadership team spend time thinking about the interconnectivity of the various job functions of each department and the dependencies that exist between them. As a communicator, oftentimes you will be involved in every area of this sometimes-tangled web, and I would encourage you to begin the dialogue about interconnectedness and integration, if the conversation has not yet happened. After all, in a public relations and crisis situation, you or a representative from your team may very well be the one standing out in front.

Don't Forget Your Co-workers: While internal communication is not the top priority in a situation as large as this one, consider assigning someone from your communications team to deliver messaging to the rest of the company through email, or the company intranet or web portal. As an employee outside the crisis, it can be disconcerting to read about your co-workers in the newspaper, or to get company updates from a press conference on television. If possible, assign an internal communications resource to act as a liaison with other communications departments, to avoid burdening the response team on the ground with multiple messages from well-meaning co-workers.

The accident in the Merrimack Valley was large enough that it gained national news attention, which attracted the attention of NiSource subsidiary companies' state regulators and local media. These entities were rightfully demanding of the company answers to the question, "If this situation happened in Massachusetts, could it happen in other areas?"

Though all of the operating companies were receiving inquiries from these regulators and news outlets, communicators had no information or approved statement to share. This put the company at risk of reputation damage in other operating companies. In addition, someone in another part of the company may have a great idea or a connection of which you were unaware and could be an extremely valuable resource. Don't lose the opportunity for critical help, guidance or feedback during a challenging time.

CHAPTER 4

ONE SIZE DOES
NOT FIT ALL

Before moving forward in the timeline of the incident and its recovery, it is important to discuss the three communities affected by the Merrimack Valley gas incident on September 13.

The city of Lawrence is the largest and most densely populated of the three communities affected by the natural gas explosions. Approximately 4,600 residential and business customers[20] in the city, south of the Merrimack River, were directly impacted by explosion, fire or loss of natural gas service for an extended period of time. According to the city of Lawrence official

---

20 Approximate customer counts in this document are referenced using the meter counts (number of meters affected by the incident. A wealth of documents pertaining to the September 13, 2018, gas incident can be found at https://www.cityoflawrence.com/718/Lawrence-Gas-Emergency.)

website,[21] Lawrence has a long history of embracing its multicultural population base, with a high percentage of its population originating from other countries including Ireland, Germany, Canada, England, Poland, Italy, Lithuania and Syria. In the mid- to late-1900s, immigrants from Puerto Rico and the Dominican Republic began arriving in the city, which is now largely Hispanic.

The following map was published in the NTSB Accident Report, *"Overpressurization of Natural Gas Distribution System, Explosions, and Fires in Merrimack Valley, Massachusetts September 13, 2018."*[22]

---

21   https://www.cityoflawrence.com/501/About-the-City.

22   https://www.ntsb.gov/investigations/AccidentReports/Reports/PAR1902.pdf, Page 2. Photo reproduced from Base map and data from OpenStreetMap and OpenStreetMap Foundation" ©OpenStreetMap Contributors. https://www.openstreetmap.org/copyright.

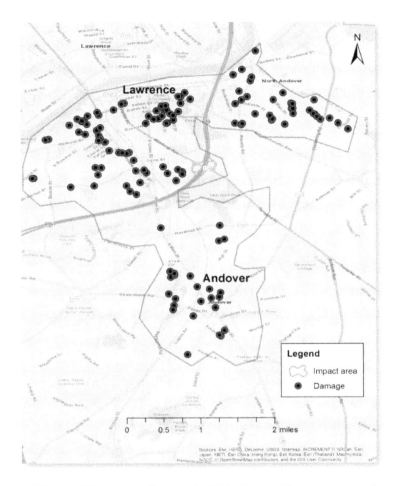

As of this writing, according to the U.S. Census Bureau, approximately 77 percent of the city of Lawrence is Hispanic or Latino. Of that Hispanic population, approximately 47 percent of residents are of Dominican descent and 21 percent are of Puerto Rican descent. The median income for a household in the city is $25,983 and the median income for a family is $29,809 (U.S. Average: $50,046). Approximately 34.3 percent of the population is below the poverty line.[23]

---

23   https://en.wikipedia.org/wiki/Lawrence,_Massachusetts

Just west of Lawrence, also south of the Merrimack River, is the town of North Andover. In contrast to the city of Lawrence, the median income for a household in the town of 28,000 is over $105,000, and approximately 5 percent of the population is below the poverty line. Nearly 88 percent of the town is Caucasian, and approximately 5 percent of the population is Hispanic or Latino.[24] In North Andover, some 1400 residential and business customers in the town were affected by the September 13 gas incident.

To the south of Lawrence lies the town of Andover, Massachusetts. Andover has a population of about 11,000 households and, according to the U.S. Census Bureau, the median income for a household in the town is over $118,000. Approximately 91 percent of the town is Caucasian, while 1.8 percent are Hispanic or Latino. For the purposes of this discussion, it should also be noted that over 200 residents of the town filed as making at least $1 million in 2011, and the average income for millionaires in Andover was $2,441,000.[25] About 1800 residential and business customers in the town were affected by the September 13 gas incident.

The concerns of three affected communities affected by the natural gas explosions were vastly different, and each of the three communities had extremely different needs related to communications.

In Lawrence, with 77 percent of the population of Latino or Hispanic descent, many of the residents spoke very little English, and some spoke no English at all. The company had not adequately anticipated this challenge, causing delays in communication to this important community. Additionally, with a higher poverty level in Lawrence than in the other two municipalities, many residents did not have the resources they needed to sustain themselves while being unable to live in their homes. Moreover, many of those affected residents did not own their homes but were renters or tenants. Some of those

---

24   https://en.wikipedia.org/wiki/North_Andover,_Massachusetts

25   https://en.wikipedia.org/wiki/Andover,_Massachusetts

tenants did not have formal leases or rental agreements. In many cases, large, multi-generational families resided together, so entire families were displaced without other options for living arrangements.

The businesses in Lawrence were not always officially registered businesses; providing legal documentation proving the ownership of and responsibility for a business to receive the necessary aid while the business was not in operation was frequently a challenge during the claims process, which we will discuss in a later chapter. Additionally, the housing infrastructure in Lawrence was older than that of Andover and North Andover, causing challenges with service restoration and appliance replacement. In general, the concerns of both residents and business owners in Lawrence were fundamental and often centered around basic survival.

At the opposite end of the spectrum, the town of Andover was home to an overwhelmingly upper-socio-economic demographic, and many of its affected residents had the ability to stay with friends and relatives and possessed the resources to survive despite this significant challenge in their lives. Residents of Andover had the ability to replace their own appliances and to utilize the claims process for reimbursement of costs.

North Andover, also an affluent community, had the least number of affected residents and businesses at approximately 1400. While not having the same level of prosperity as many of the residents of Andover, and being infinitely better off than many of the residents of Lawrence, North Andover oftentimes seemed to fall in the middle of the struggle for resources.

It should be noted that it is not my intent to indicate that the concerns of Andover or North Andover were lesser than the concerns of Lawrence. Every person and family affected by this situation had challenges to overcome. This section is merely intended to outline the extreme differences between the three communities.

KEY TAKEAWAYS
(Lessons Learned)

The Path to Intelligent Response: No matter your industry, company or discipline, before a crisis hits, know the demographic makeup of your customers or affected population. While CMA external and government affairs partners were certainly aware of the makeup of the three towns, in the heat of the crisis no one was immediately thinking about having documents translated into Spanish, let alone into a Dominican dialect of Spanish. While the company pivoted as quickly as possible on document translation, an early opportunity was missed to connect and build trust with community members and leaders.

Method of Message Delivery: Take the time to understand how your customers would like to receive their information. As the restoration and recovery process progressed and once the company was able to become more organized, CMA tried to get updates out to the public in as many ways as possible—website, social media, door tags, through community resources partners, press releases, etc.—because so much of the information was vital to safety. But the messages were slightly different for each community, depending upon individual and community needs. Likewise, in any crisis, it is likely that different segments of the audience will need individualized communication. If you can determine those audiences and their differences through a proactive stakeholder analysis early on, you will be better off overall.

Access to Messaging: These days, we tend to think largely in terms of technological delivery of messaging, but in some economically disadvantaged areas of the country, many residents don't have the same access to technology. Equipment may be too expensive, training may be lacking and broadband may be limited. While website updates and social media messaging are important and vital ways to deliver information, they shouldn't be your only consideration.

Personal Communications: Get out into the community and talk to residents as quickly as possible after a crisis occurs to assess their needs. Again, the scale of this incident was so large it was extremely difficult to adequately assess the immediate community impact. And while driving personal relationships with customers or stakeholders isn't necessarily a communications responsibility, understanding the needs of the community is a key responsibility, and it will prove vital to implementing an effective communications strategy through the most effective and relevant channels.

CHAPTER 5

AND THE TIDE STARTED TO TURN

Residents who were evacuated from the impacted area were able to return to their homes by 7:00 am EDT on September 16, 2018, three days after the incident, but restoration of residential natural gas and electricity service required more time and involved multiple steps to coordinate the activities safely. At that time, another gas company was overseeing the restoration and recovery effort, but until the gas service was restored, affected customers were still without heat and hot water. They also weren't able to use other gas-fueled appliances like clothes dryers and stoves.

In September of 2018, the weather in Massachusetts was still quite warm, and the company was optimistic that winter weather would not become a concern in the restoration timeline. But it had become clear that not all customers could return to their homes if unable to cook meals or take a hot shower.

According to the *Merrimack Valley Natural Gas Explosions After Action Report*, published by MEMA, the Recovery Resource Center (RRC) was opened in Lawrence to provide impacted residents access to various programs and resources. This Center opened on Sunday, September 16 and was co-located with an American Red Cross emergency shelter, providing support for physical, emotional, financial and other needs. On Tuesday, September 18, due to overcrowding, the RRC was moved to the Lawrence Elks Lodge, and separated from the emergency shelter. As residents received the early resources they needed for basic survival and some sense of normalcy began to return, the RRC closed on Friday, September 21.

Beginning on Sunday, September 16 and throughout that week, Columbia Gas opened three dedicated claims centers for residents of all three communities and established a hotline and website that offered information and assistance for affected residents. While two earlier claims centers had been attempted, these initial efforts to establish helpful services were overwhelmed by the number of residents seeking assistance. During the week of September 16, CMA officials, supported by local government partners and security personnel, were able to offer help to affected residents in a more coordinated fashion. The establishment of the claims centers, the Red Cross emergency shelter, and the RRC were happening simultaneously in the communities.

On Tuesday, September 18, the Massachusetts governor announced the implementation of the Greater Lawrence Disaster Relief Fund. Columbia Gas publicized its contribution of $10 million to this fund, which was managed by the Essex County Community Foundation.[26] This marked the first time that leaders from Columbia Gas appeared jointly with local elected officials, community leaders and the governor.

It was also during this week the governor activated the Massachusetts National Guard to help with "Operation Hotplate" and "Operation Temporary Heat," both efforts to provide basic cooking and heating tools to affected residents through the distribution of hotplates and space heaters until gas service could be restored. While the distribution efforts did not begin until Saturday, September 22, the announcement of these initiatives earlier in the week were met with mostly positive reactions from residents and officials in the affected communities.

---

26   https://www.eccf.org/

Meanwhile, at the NiSource headquarters and subsidiary companies, while employees were still, for the most part, receiving their updates from the local news, the company had begun to strengthen internal communications through regular calls with communications counterparts who had been deployed to support ground efforts in Massachusetts. Twice-daily calls with the team on the ground were established, and the team identified a communications liaison whom communications employees could contact for questions and concerns from other parts of the organization. State communications leads were able work with their subsidiary presidents to communicate with employee populations, and teams had begun drafting responses to individual state regulatory bodies, which had inevitably started reaching out with questions about the incident.

During the same week, the company began to construct a schedule of communication resources that would support the ongoing work in Massachusetts. Because NiSource still did not know the full scope of the restoration work, it seemed as though a month-long weekly rotation of company communication resources would be sufficient to support communication needs during the restoration and recovery effort.

Encouragingly, after the power was restored on Sunday, September 16, and CMA began to exhibit a greater sense of control over the situation, discussions took place regarding restoring control of the restoration and recovery effort to Columbia Gas and NiSource. This was a welcome development, and it finally felt as though the company had started to regain its authority. While residents of Lawrence, Andover and North Andover may not have trusted the company at that point, there was a sense the company had begun repairing damaged relationships and broken trust.

KEY TAKEAWAYS
(Lessons Learned)

Do the Right Thing: Stepping up and taking ownership of corporate social responsibility is extremely important in crisis situations. While not every organization will have $10 million to give to a community fund, neither will every crisis require this level of commitment. Even so, it is important that you help to assess the situation and the needs of the community based on your company's role in the crisis and respond accordingly. While this is not a suggestion that community giving in this instance was only a public relations move, taking responsibility can only help with reputation management. At the end of the day, if a company is willing to do the right thing, reputation management and positive public relations should follow (not the other way around).

But take care to understand that compensation alone will not solve your reputation problems. If the effort is seen as insincere or as tokenism, monetary contributions could have the opposite intended effect and be perceived negatively. Careful consideration needs to be made regarding the determination of any contribution, the contribution recipient and the way that the contribution is made and announced (if it is announced at all).

Rebuild the Bridge: If you find yourself in a situation during which an attempt to make up for a lack of response or to regain control after a PR stumble, continued efforts to repair relationships with key stakeholders will begin to pay off. In this case, Columbia Gas increased its communication with public officials, and as the company began to understand more about the task ahead, company leadership was able to coordinate in a more organized fashion. That is not to say that the relationships were repaired. Far from it. But it was during this time of reorganization and partnership that the company was able to start to make some decisions that paved the way for collaboration. Columbia Gas recognized its initial missteps with communications and made sincere efforts to repair the damage that had been done. While not all entities were interested in forgiving and forgetting, there was recognition that Columbia Gas and NiSource were attempting to do the right thing, and there was grudging acceptance of those efforts.

Continuous Learning Is Key: As a natural gas utility, wide-spread effort to address thousands of claims issues was not an expertise the company possessed. But after initially attempting to serve overwhelmed, scared, emotional and hurting residents, many of whom did not speak English, during its first attempt to set up a claims center, the company assessed its needs and was able to begin the process for a more organized response. Bringing on experts who were experienced with large-scale disasters, such as natural disaster response, allowed CMA to oversee the claims organization, while claims processors who were familiar with restoration and recovery efforts handled the detailed work. Although this is not specifically a communications take-away, it is worth noting that the ability to be agile and pivot quickly is important in all areas of crisis response (including communications), and paying attention to areas that need improvement should be a goal of every team member.

CHAPTER 6

LEADERSHIP MATTERS

By Tuesday, September 18, five days after the initial incident, Columbia Gas had not yet restored natural gas service to those customers directly affected by the incident. The company was in the process of trying to repair its relationships with the communities and public officials. NiSource and Columbia Gas had stepped up and donated money, time and resources. Hundreds of company employees from both Massachusetts and NiSource's six state subsidiary companies were on the ground and working out of the established command center at its Marston Street site located immediately off Interstate 495 in Lawrence. But as discussions continued to take place over the week, it was clear that the scope of this situation was much larger and more serious than most had anticipated. It was certainly more serious than the communities had realized, and residents and businesses were becoming increasingly frustrated that nearly a week after the incident, gas service still had not been restored to their properties. Businesses were losing income and customers, and residents were still staying with friends and families or making do with limited resources and cold showers. The governor, who was onsite at the command center almost daily, knew that the situation was bigger than any one entity could handle on its own.

On Friday, September 21, through his Emergency Declaration, the governor officially announced that retired Navy Captain Joe Albanese, founder and CEO of Commodore Builders, a large commercial construction firm, would serve as the Chief Recovery Officer (CRO) for the project. Albanese served over 25 years with the Naval Construction Forces, during which he led more than 2,200 Navy Seabees throughout the Middle East in 2007.

Perhaps most importantly, Albanese had deep ties to Massachusetts. He was born and raised just outside of Boston, attended a local university, and raised a family and headquartered a business in the area. He also served on several boards of well-known non-profits in the Greater Boston area and was well-connected to the veterans' community.[27] Albanese spoke and thought like a Bostonian. Local leadership trusted and respected him, residents and business owners knew that Albanese was one of them, and that recognition and familiarity went a long way in establishing trust in the mission that was about to take place.

---

27 Commodore Builders official website and Joe Albanese Biography, https://commodorebuilders.com/people/joseph-j-albanese/, November 2022.

Chief Recovery Officer Joe Albanese speaks as the Mass. Governor, North Andover Town Manager and Andover Town Manager look on. Photo credit: Tim Jean/Boston Media Group

The role of CRO proved challenging for several reasons. As CRO, Albanese was to oversee the repair of pipelines and the re-establishment of gas service to affected residents and businesses in Lawrence, Andover and North Andover. He was additionally responsible for coordinating with government officials, and managing thousands of people from diverse locations, backgrounds and companies, most of whom he had never met and who had never worked together. Not only did the task at hand, which had not yet been fully established, loom large, but the majority of the massive team had never participated in an event of this size. Albanese was leading many people who had never experienced a crisis before, let alone an event of this magnitude.

Albanese, who had no formal gas utility experience himself, realized the scope of the recovery, and he established an organizational structure and support mechanisms to manage each unique need. He brought in several trusted confidants from his previous military background to help him organize and execute the work in front of him. And notably, he included senior members of the NiSource executive and leadership team as a part of his own leadership structure, quickly establishing relationships and rapport that he would need to lean on throughout the recovery effort.

Early on, a formal organizational structure for work groups had not been strictly implemented because of the ever-changing nature of the crisis. By the time Albanese had been formally installed on September 21, 2018, the need for organization, integration and collaboration was clear. The new organizational structure encompassed several areas: construction, operations, social services, mitigation, customer support/relations, communications, and support services that ranged from catering and facilities to tiger team[28] implementation. This structure was highly flexible and expanded as necessary to include additional areas of the ongoing recovery effort.

Similar to the Incident Commander role in the Federal Emergency Management Agency (FEMA) Incident Command System (ICS) structure,[29] CRO Albanese was tasked with managing the overall scope of the disaster situation, including communications. He had a vested stake in ensuring communications functions contributed to the success of the mission. From a communications perspective, the establishment of the CRO role and structure were critical to the ability to get information quickly to customers and the public at large. It established a single point of contact to which the communications team had access, and from which the team could get information quickly.

With the appointment of the CRO, the communications role was recognized as extending beyond simply responding to the media and updating the website. Albanese understood the importance of a coordinated and comprehensive response to all parties, with customers at the forefront of that

---

28   https://en.wikipedia.org/wiki/Tiger_team

29   Federal Emergency Management Agency (FEMA): https://www.fema.gov/sites/default/files/2020-07/fema_nims_doctrine-2017.pdf.

response. He knew that information given to public officials needed to exactly match what the company was telling customers directly and reporting to the media. He also understood that any remarks he made in public must exactly mirror what was being said in private briefings with public individuals, and that relationships were key to all of these aspects of reputation management. While the CRO's primary focus was always to ensure heat and hot water were restored quickly and safely to the affected residents and businesses, a secondary goal immediately followed—repair the damage that had been done to personal and professional reputations by delivering on goals and communicating transparently, often, consistently and accurately.

At the command center in the Marston Street location, employees and contractors assessed what would become the restoration phase of the crisis and worked to determine what efforts would be necessary to get people safely back into their homes. As the picture of the crisis became clearer, having stepped up and back into its responsibilities, Columbia Gas once again became the leading utility on the ground.

But while the immediate emergency had abated, the situation was far from over. As the week progressed, assessments had determined that the entire 45-mile low-pressure pipeline system, which had been damaged by the incident, needed to be replaced. For context, 45 miles of pipeline replacement is approximately the amount of infrastructure replacement work that would typically take place in an entire year in the CMA service territory.[30]

Secondly, as the company had begun to perform in-home assessments of natural gas appliances, it was determined that each and every natural gas

---

30 For more information on natural gas replacement programs, review "Natural Gas Infrastructure Modernization Programs at Local Distribution Companies: Key Issues and Considerations Office of Energy Policy and Systems Analysis," U.S. Department of Energy Washington, DC 20585 January, 2017: https://www.energy.gov/sites/prod/files/2017/01/ f34/Natural%20Gas%20Infrastructure%20Modernization%20Programs%20at%20 Local%20Distribution%20Companies--Key%20Issues%20and%20Considerations.pdf

appliance owned by every affected customer in the Merrimack Valley would be replaced. This encompassed over 10,000 affected dwellings in Lawrence, Andover and North Andover. Appliances designated for replacement were gas ranges, gas dryers, gas furnaces or boilers, along with any other ancillary natural gas appliances such as fireplaces or pool heaters.

If you happen to be a natural gas customer, you know that most natural gas utility and distribution companies do not service your gas appliances past the meter (and in many areas of the country, customers are responsible for their own service line maintenance). This "behind the meter" work was not something with which Columbia Gas employees had experience. Furthermore, commercial customers such as restaurants and other types of businesses had vastly different natural gas needs than residential customers.

The scope of this project itself was massive, and while the weather in the third week of September 2018 was still very warm, public officials, emergency responders, and the restoration leadership knew that the weather in the Northeast could turn bitterly cold very quickly. While company leadership had not initially thought that timing and weather would be an issue, the team was now operating under a critical timeline.

Complicating the situation, Operation Temporary Heat and Operation Hotplate, which had offered some early assistance to customers, had run into insurmountable challenges to success. While both efforts had begun as a means to allow residential customers to stay in their homes during the restoration efforts, according to the "Merrimack Valley Natural Gas Explosions After Action Report" published by the MEMA, "critical safety concerns were not identified prior to the initial selection and procurement of space heaters... It was quickly realized that many of the older homes in the area did not have the electrical service needed to safely operate space heaters."[31] The assessments and requirements to ensure that space heaters could safely be installed in homes proved more onerous than beneficial and was discontinued as a standalone program on September 28. Only 192 space heaters were ultimately installed. Operation Hotplate continued in a modified fashion, with about 7,500 hotplates being delivered to residents of Lawrence, Andover and North Andover.

With the abandonment of Operation Temporary Heat and Operation Hotplate came a flurry of negative press and criticism from local officials that the company did not have the organization or coordination necessary for success. The communications team was once again front and center in a defensive position.

From a communications organization perspective, at this point, the team struggled with how communications fit into the overall structure of the Restoration and Recovery team and how the team itself was structured and managed. Even though the communications function fell under the purview of the CRO, he felt strongly that an employee of NiSource or Columbia Gas should be responsible for communications for the purpose of reputation management. He was right, but the team also struggled with organization and management of communications contract resources, many of whom had been summoned by various well-meaning members of the Restoration and Recovery team. With so many crises taking place, the communications team was under pressure and falling behind.

The threat of winter weather also loomed large with the recognition of the enormity of the amount of pipeline and appliance replacement. With another public relations challenge in the form of the discontinued Operation

---

31   From the "Merrimack Valley Natural Gas Explosions After Action Report September 13 - December 16, 2018," published by the Massachusetts Emergency Management Agency: https://www.mass.gov/doc/merrimack-valley-natural-gas-explosions-after-action-report/download https://www.mass.gov/doc/merrimack-valley-natural-gas-explosions-after-action-report/download, Page 8.

Temporary Heat in the local news, there was incredible pressure on the newly appointed CRO to ensure the mission was a success—that residents would be back in their homes, and businesses would be up and running quickly. Not only was it imperative that he meet this goal, but it was also critical the plan was communicated in a way that instilled confidence in both the path forward and the ongoing efforts of the Merrimack Valley Restoration and Recovery team. This included not only affected residents and customers, but federal, state and local elected officials, the Massachusetts Department of Public Utilities, emergency responders, social services agencies, industry stakeholders and the general public.

KEY TAKEAWAYS
(Lessons Learned)

A Single Source: It is imperative during a crisis situation that the communications person or team responsible for responding to the public have *one* identified source from which to receive updates and information; otherwise, the team will struggle to not only obtain information, but to obtain consistent and clear information. As a communicator, if you can't access clear, consistent messaging, it becomes difficult to confidently portray to the public or other stakeholders the details that will help them stay informed.

Early on in the crisis, the situation was so large and chaotic that it was difficult to receive the correct and necessary information, and that was evident during the public response. With the appointment of the CRO, an established organization began to take shape, and this streamlined and simplified the goals of everyone on the team.

The Right Source: Likewise, it is imperative during a crisis situation that the *right* person be placed in a position of authority. For example, under the FEMA structure, this person is the Incident Commander. As a communicator, if you aren't getting the clear and consistent messaging you need, you certainly have the ability and the obligation to report any difficulties up the chain of command.

In a situation like the one in the Merrimack Valley, the appointment of the CRO established the clear leadership of someone with a background that included: 1) leadership of a large company that dealt with complex construction projects, 2) military experience—a veteran military officer, who had risen through the ranks and served as both a part of a team and the leader of thousands working toward a common goal, and 3) familiarity with the affected communities and the greater urban area—someone who was well-respected and who could speak with authority, relevancy and credibility.

Face It: Someone must be the "face" of the situation. As discussed earlier, the role of the communications organization is to ensure the public and/or identified stakeholders receive the correct updates and the information they need. The job of communicator, unless explicitly identified, is not to take ownership of the situation itself or to present himself or herself as the face of the company. In most well-managed crises, the executive in charge (usually the CEO or a member of the C-suite) becomes the face of the situation for the company—the public figure who *is* the company. In the Merrimack Valley, the crisis overtook the corporation of NiSource or Columbia Gas as an entity. While the company was ultimately responsible for the crisis and its aftermath, the vast scope of the situation (community, social, industry, political, customer, financial) became overwhelming for any one entity to manage alone, especially with a lack of experience in an event of such scale. Albanese had the experience and the gravitas to become the trusted face of the restoration and recovery effort. From a communications perspective, this development made the job of the communications team easier and ultimately led to (arguably) milder press coverage.

Listen to the People Who Matter: One theme that remains throughout any discussion of the Merrimack Valley disaster is the pervasive need to accept input from local communities. In the case of Operation Temporary Heat, which distributed space heaters to the communities, a more thorough understanding of the communities, their infrastructures and the demographics would have been helpful before implementing the program, which was well-intentioned but ultimately unsuccessful and required public response and defense.

While the communications team on the ground may not have been consulted about the decision to implement Operation Temporary Heat, the team was once again put in the position of responding to public criticism and attempting to mitigate damage. This situation highlights the need for a communicator to be involved in *every* aspect of the ongoing work from the beginning, through implementation and, ultimately, resolution. Even if not acting as an ultimate decision-maker, involvement and exposure for the communications team at the initial stages of any crisis mitigation effort can allow for a more swift and accurate response.

Work Toward the Same Goal: We've discussed the need for coordination across departments, but coordination amongst the communications team during a crisis is just as critical. With so many different teams from Columbia Gas, NiSource and other communications consulting companies on the ground responsible for leading different aspects of communications for the ongoing crisis, they were not always aligned by one single point of leadership. Compounding that was the rotation of NiSource and Columbia

Gas employees who were brought in to help in weekly shifts, left largely on their own with little guidance, while attempting to understand the scope and complications of the entire effort. Communications participants new to the crisis spent most of their time observing and trying to understand how best to contribute to the work. It was obvious that one clear leader for communications, who had a good handle on the task before him or her, and the assignments and abilities of each contract partner, would have been extremely beneficial during this crucial time of crisis, to provide some level of consistency for the communications professionals, both employee and contract, on the ground.

CHAPTER 7

THE PLAN GOES PUBLIC WHILE THE CRISIS CONTINUES

While the pace for the employees and contractors on the ground in Massachusetts had not abated, for affected residents in the Merrimack Valley, the continued lack of natural gas service continued to impact lives and livelihoods. Businesses had been suspended or shut down completely, impacting not only those business owners, but their employees who may or may not have been affected themselves. Family routines had to be drastically altered to deal with the interruption to daily life. Residents who were not able to inhabit their homes were forced to navigate new work and school commutes and transportation needs and routines. Not everyone had relatives nearby where they may have been able to drop in for a hot shower or hot meal.

Columbia Gas had established a process to file claims and had employed national experts on filing and handling claims for items such as loss of wages, food and living expenses, hotel rooms, and transportation costs. But like any large-scale administrative process, things did not always go smoothly or quickly. Affected residents and communities were frustrated.

By this time, national public attention had largely subsided, due partly to the destruction caused by Hurricane Florence, which brought devastating flooding to the Carolinas in September 2018. Even though attention had been broadly averted, local Merrimack Valley and Boston media were still keen to report on every aspect of the process of recovery for the residents who had been impacted by the incident.

The new project leadership team, led by CRO Albanese, pushed the team on the ground to work out a plan quickly. On October 2, 2018, nearly three weeks after the incident in the Merrimack Valley, Columbia Gas of Massachusetts publicly announced its "Gas Ready" plan for the replacement of over 45 miles of underground cast iron and bare steel pipe and over 5,000 customer service lines, along with the successful pressure testing of over 12 miles of polyethylene main pipe. The plan also included the deployment of nearly 200 construction crews as part of a combined workforce of about 3,000 employees and contractors, aiming to complete the project by November 19, 2018, with systematic and synchronized restoration of customers' gas service.

Several days later, on October 5, 2018, the company publicly shared additional information regarding the plan to restore gas service to customers in the Merrimack Valley, which included planned assessments and appliance installations in coordination with the previously announced Gas Ready construction schedule. The plan, labeled, "House Ready,"[32] outlined details for the in-home and in-business assessments, appliance installations and

---

32   The Gas Ready and House Ready announcements and plans can be found here: https://www.cityoflawrence.com/718/Lawrence-Gas-Emergency.

the final safety checks required to restore gas service, and was intended to align with the Gas Ready plan scheduled to be completed by November 19.[33]

As a part of the House Ready work, one large contract partner that had performed extensive previous work in service restoration for natural disasters was assigned to the project.

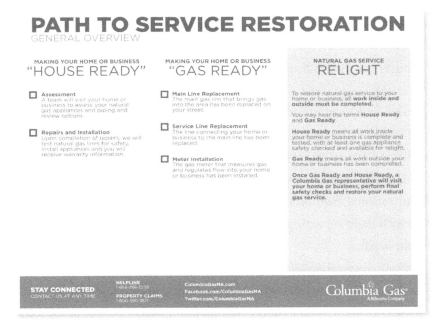

This contractor implemented a block approach—assigning crews in the field to follow a structured plan in the affected communities where crews would then disconnect and remove damaged appliances, repair or replace in-home gas lines, and connect new appliances to make the home ready to be reconnected to gas service.

In conjunction with these announcements, the company also prepared to introduce an interactive map, which would enable customers to check

---

33   https://www.cityoflawrence.com/DocumentCenter/View/4008/
      Columbia-Gas-House-Ready-slide-deck--10-5-2018_FINAL.

the status of projects at their homes and in their neighborhood in real-time.

To coordinate both pipeline replacement and House Ready work, the affected area was divided into eight sections or "zones," and each zone was assigned at least two zone commanders who were tasked with canvassing their assigned zone and reporting back any concerns taking place within that particular area. Zone commanders were experienced and skilled gasmen and women, most of whom had decades of experience in natural gas operations and construction work, and who were all well-versed in the operation of a natural gas distribution system and could explain the concept in terms understandable by the public. The zone commanders were empowered to connect with community residents and leaders, to make decisions in the field and to bring information directly back to the command center. These men and women were the eyes and ears in the field for the leadership team.

The eight zones served by the zone commanders would become the organizational method for the rest of the restoration project and the way by which daily reporting to elected officials and city and town leadership would occur.

From September 13 to September 30, I had been on the ground in the Merrimack Valley twice—once in the role of communications support for a week and again to fill in as chief of staff for another executive for a week. During these two weeks, I had the opportunity to not only draft communications—talking points, press releases, fact sheets, and website posts and updates, but I had the opportunity to observe. Publicly, we were in a better place than we had been during the first days following the explosions. The leadership of the new executive team, along with their specialized organizational skills and planning methods, had restored some confidence with both local public officials and the affected customers.

But while the communications function had gotten better, it appeared as though the improvement was more the result of the newly implemented plans rather than the result of improved communications processes and structure.

In fact, there was clearly a gap in the way communications was working, even in the midst of an improved public presence.

Firstly, the company still employed multiple communications consultants who were subject to less oversight than the company's internal communications team. Individually, these were all superb communications professionals, but with a lack of guidance and coordination, none of the consultants were contributing to their full potential.

Also, the company was still flying in and assigning internal communications personnel in weekly shifts. While in theory and on paper this should have worked, because of the complex and ever-changing nature of the project, communicators new to the effort had trouble getting up to speed quickly. The lack of a single source of communications leadership left capable communications professionals wondering how they could best contribute and provide value.

Thirdly, in a bid to gain some control over the situation, a company executive had hired a consultant that had both local and federal ties to contribute to the communications effort. This consultant was primarily responsible for media relations. While media relations were a crucial element of the overall communications plan, the overarching need was much larger than only repairing damaged relationships with the press. There was an enormous need to lead the dozens of communications professionals on the ground, provide a single point of leadership, and represent the company both internally and with external stakeholders. The company still needed a leader to bring all of the communications elements together. As we've learned, interdependencies are the key to success, especially in a crisis as big and complex as this one, and with as much need for tight and integrated communications.

In my role as temporary chief of staff, and outside of the immediate communications function, I was free to observe these dynamics and think about the best course of action. I took my concerns to the two most senior company communications employees on the ground at the time. Both of these long-time employees and seasoned communicators found themselves in a challenging position because they had not officially been placed in a position of any formal authority. And with the arrival of the newest external consultant, they were powerless to make substantial changes.

Most importantly, while this internal instability within the communications function was taking place, public officials had continued to alert the restoration leadership team and the CRO that customers were not getting the most important information in the way they preferred. Project updates needed to be communicated to both the affected and the general public through multiple channels, including face-to-face interactions, news channels (press releases), social media, word-of-mouth, advertising, social services agencies, among other tactics. Even with a solid principal plan in place, because the communications team itself hadn't been firmly instituted and integrated, the company was missing key elements of communications and an integrated approach.

With only a few days before I was scheduled to return home, I felt the need to address the important issue of a lack of communications structure and a personal responsibility to attempt to raise the issue through the proper channels.

I approached another senior executive who was in a position of some authority, and with whom I felt comfortable sharing my concern. She agreed with me, though part of the challenge was that every person on the ground had their own massive issues to deal with, and communications, while a priority for the company, wasn't necessarily *the* priority for any individual leader.

This executive listened to my concerns and agreed to have a conversation with me, as well as with other members of the executive leadership team. The team committed to addressing the concerns, which they too had noticed but had not been prompted to act upon.

I traveled back home feeling as though I had done my part.

A day later, I was at a co-worker's wedding on a Saturday afternoon when I received a call from the chief restoration officer, asking me to return to the

Merrimack Valley, this time for the remainder of the crisis, to help lead the communications effort.

As a single parent with a sixteen-year-old son at home, this was difficult, but honestly, I didn't overthink my answer. There was no question that I was going to do what needed to be done for the company. So, the next day, two days after I'd returned from the Merrimack Valley, I was heading back again to take on a new challenge.

KEY TAKEAWAYS
(Lessons Learned)

Modify Your Structure as Needed: The creation of the position of zone commander was arguably one of the greatest successes of the restoration effort itself, with the commanders acting in leadership roles both across their communities and internally, reporting out daily issues and situations that needed to be immediately addressed by the restoration leadership team. Not only did the CRO heavily rely on the information shared by the zone commanders, but the communications team also used that information to streamline communications and tailor messaging to individual audiences.

From a communications standpoint, it's important to look for ways to streamline your own functions in similar manners. Think about natural divisions of responsibilities or geography across your territories. Are there organizational structures within your own teams occurring in a crisis or even in day-to-day operations that make sense from a responsibility standpoint? In addition to the roles that your team holds, think about the organization of your team. Don't be afraid to make or suggest changes that could simplify or enhance your function. It's never too late to make alterations that may contribute to success.

Keep It Simple: Make the communications materials as simple and as understandable as possible for your audience. While the normal process for the distribution of natural gas is not an overly complex one, most people don't spend a lot of time understanding the way that their utilities operate. The Gas Ready and House Ready plans, in my opinion, were brilliant examples of simplifying what had become a multi-step process of pipeline repairs and ensuing home repairs and relights.

No matter the industry in which you work, if the general public or customers are affected, you will likely have the same concerns. Keeping communications consistent and simple, especially when they involve actions or processes, will allow you to easily repurpose that messaging across multiple audiences and will save time by avoiding the need to continuously explain your communications.

An example of the "Path to Service Restoration" overview can be found at the Mass.Gov official website at: https://www.mass.gov/doc/columbia-gas-path-to-service-restoration-overview/download. Over the course of the restoration and recovery phase, the "Path to Service Restoration" overview evolved into a 20-page booklet, printed in English and Spanish, with information on the Gas Ready and House Ready processes, what to expect, how customers could replace their own appliances (self-mitigate), how to file a claim, the process customers needed to follow to be set up with temporary housing, a list of available appliances, contact information, and important safety information. As we learned what was needed in the community, more information was added and was provided to the public through multiple channels.

Say Something: As a communicator, if you see the function suffering, speak up. I've worked for companies and leaders who highly valued communications teams, and I've worked for organizations and executives who felt that anyone at all could perform the communications function. I've had to speak up in both types of situations when I've felt as though a project was headed for troubled waters. In the case of the Merrimack Valley, I knew the project couldn't be as successful as it needed to be without centralized communications leadership. The situation was too complex, and there were too many communicators on the ground without real understanding of their role. And by not having a central communications leader, the company appeared to be unprepared to face the public ramifications and start taking hold of reputation management.

By raising my hand, I certainly put myself in the position of a volunteer to do work that was a major challenge—mentally, emotionally, professionally and personally. But if faced with the same choice today, I'd make the same decision in a heartbeat. By speaking up and getting the conversation started, I affected a change in the organizational structure that ultimately made long-term improvements for the entire project. I can look back and see the value that my voice provided.

Take Ownership: Consultants can be a great supplement to your team, but at the end of the day, it's the *company's* reputation that on the line, not the consultant's reputation. CRO Albanese understood that while he was responsible for the mission to get affected customers back into their homes safely before winter, the company and its reputation would live on long after he was gone. A consultant doesn't typically have the same commitment that a full-time employee has, nor will he/she understand the employees, relationships, core business and necessary connections. It can be tempting to cede authority to an outside entity who claims to have the expertise to handle any situation. Even if that entity does have the expertise, I've always been of the opinion that it's better to learn from those expert organizations and improve my own skills rather than hand over control and decision-making to another organization.

It's worth thinking about the way you use consultants in your day-to-day operations, as well as how a consultant might serve you in a crisis. Does it make sense to develop a relationship with a crisis communications firm who can help you proactively develop the procedures and materials you might need? Developing a lasting relationship with a consultancy well-versed in crisis communications might allow you to get to a place where you can handle a crisis on your own with confidence.

Take Personal Chances: This is more of a personal word of advice rather than advice centered on communications, but when an opportunity to lead is presented to you, take it. When I got that call just before the start of a wedding ceremony on a Saturday afternoon, there wasn't the slightest hesitation in my answer. There were many reasons for that. I may have been flattered, but I was also sure I could make a difference for those customers who were displaced, many of whom were confused, angry and scared. I knew it was going to be challenging, but most things worth doing aren't easy. They require commitment, focus, concentration and dedication. Often, they require difficult conversations and sleepless nights. Sometimes they require tears. I experienced all those things in the Merrimack Valley, and I would do it all again.

CHAPTER 8

POLITICAL AND PERSONAL MOTIVATIONS

Two days after my previous trip to the Merrimack Valley, I arrived back in the command center, this time with a daunting task in front of me. Luckily, I wasn't alone. Another communications director was by my side as we took on this new leadership challenge, and she became my partner, my confidant, and will always be a true friend.

We first decided that one of us would always be onsite. That meant the project and command center would never be left without a communications leader on the ground. It meant more time away from our families, and it also meant long nights and early mornings, but it was important and necessary work. And we were relatively fresh-faced and ready to tackle any challenge.

Overhauling the communications process was a big job. My counterpart took on the more tactical work of assessing the numbers and skillsets of the communications employees and consultants who were supporting the work, while I tackled the more strategic work of instituting a plan to connect all areas of communications with the work that needed to be done.

We divided the work into External (social media, media, and community/legislative tasks) and Internal (restoration and employee) and assigned both Columbia Gas/NiSource and consulting partner leads to each. We then began the task of tracking the communication professionals onsite and assigning them work specific to each workstream —social media, customer communications, temporary housing, claims, back to business, construction, house ready, relights, media, internal, call center, executive, website and community/legislative. Some of us were overseeing and working for multiple areas. For example, I took on much of the executive and customer communications work and my counterpart took on community/legislative and call center communications support, while we jointly oversaw the entire communications organization.

We also took the time to perform a stakeholder analysis to ensure we were meeting the communications needs of all possible audiences, both internally and externally. We kept in mind that each audience had different concerns and motivations, but at the end of the day the residential and business customers without heat and hot water were our primary audience, and the audience through which all other communications materials must be developed. Subgroups existed within that group of customers. For example, customers who had decided to make repairs on their own (self-mitigators) may have been one subgroup of customers needing unique messaging, and Spanish-speaking customers who were renting an affected property while staying in temporary housing would have been another subset of affected customers requiring specialized communications.

Based on our assessments, our organizational chart looked something like the following chart that outlines a high-level depiction of responsibilities. The work was much more complex than is illustrated here, but the information gives you an idea of the way we approached the division of stake-holders and responsibilities. You will notice that we include both responsible parties from the company as well as our consulting partners.

COMMUNICATIONS STRATEGY TEAM RESPONSIBILITIES Company Communications Lead Consulting Partner Communications Lead					
	External Communication			Internal Communications	
	Social	Media	Community/ Legislative	Restoration/ Recovery Team	Company
Responsibility	Provide proactive social media outreach and timely, effective response to inquiries and comments	Respond to media inquiries and provide proactive, positive outreach to broad audiences	Provide direct outreach to and relationship-building with community officials through multiple forums; Collaborate with govt affairs personnel to respond to inquiries and identify opportunities for engagement This position requires the creation of talking points and other materials	Develop materials and proactively share information and updates with project team; Align with project partners and address immediate needs including special projects and emergent requests	Inform company personnel (outside of project response efforts) of project updates and challenges This may include executive leadership team, company officers and board of directors
Company Lead	Responsible employee	Responsible employee	Responsible employee	Responsible employee	Responsible employee
Consulting Partner Lead	Responsible partner	Responsible partner	Responsible partner	Responsible partner	Responsible partner

We assessed each individual communicator onsite, and we accounted for the time employees and consultants could devote to the project, and how they interacted with both their communications teammates and project leaders. We also considered how well each employee and consultant could manage their workload as well as themselves. In other words, we needed self-starters and communications professionals who could get things done quickly and didn't need constant reassurance or direction. Employees and consultants who didn't push projects through to completion sometimes were not asked back to help.

Additionally, if a communications professional had trouble managing the many personalities with whom he or she needed to interact on any given day, that employee was either re-assigned to another part of the overall project or given project work to complete at a home office, if necessary.

While most everyone on the restoration team was working toward the same goal of restoring heat and hot water to affected customers' homes, there were individuals onsite who had their own agendas for wanting to be a part of the project. Some people were there for the visibility—company executives were present daily and company board of director members also visited the work sites and the command centers as the work progressed. Others were there for professional development or networking opportunities, and some consultants were there because it was a lucrative endeavor.

While the main reason for my own continued involvement was to help the affected customers, an additional motivation for accepting the assignment was simply to see if I could succeed. It was a personal challenge. I had the right background and mindset to get the work done, but I knew the experience would test me in ways I'd never been tested before. It certainly did that and more.

These myriad reasons for being part of the work, on the part of both employees and consultants, created interesting relationships, and it was often challenging to navigate those relationships in the face of tight deadlines and intense internal and external pressure. Some employees and consultants performed better than others in this environment.

While writing this book, I discovered that those who were invited to come back on a regular basis (and for consistency of messaging and routine, we did try to keep the same people on the team) felt that if you had not been invited back— or worse, had never been invited at all—you weren't a part of the "A" team. Looking back, I can understand how employees may have felt that way. At the time though, we were simply trying to get work done. It had nothing to do with individuals' feelings or egos.

By mid-October, I felt as if we had created a highly functioning communications team that had been organized by skillset and commitment, who understood the mission, could handle the workload, and were willing to change direction quickly in terms of assignment and strategy.

KEY TAKEAWAYS
(Lessons Learned)

Step Back: Communications is never a standalone function, but in a crisis situation, it is imperative that a holistic view of every aspect of communication is considered to adequately plan for every possible scenario. It can be difficult to stop the work at hand, especially in a fast-moving crisis, but taking a step back to assess the various aspects of the situation to develop or alter the strategy can be helpful to overall mission success. Implementing a predetermined structure for the communications function can help to avoid the need to pause during important response work for a discussion about strategy. Ensure your structure is made to be flexible and fluid, and that positions can be added or subtracted based upon your unique circumstances.

Consider Other Players: In any situation where communications is asked to support, a stakeholder analysis is necessary. Nuanced messaging will be needed for internal and external audiences. Internal audiences will expect a more technical presentation of the crisis and solutions, whereas external audiences will most likely require a high-level, general message and information relevant to their personal situations. Additionally, the risks will be different for unique audiences. Your investor community will require different messaging than the media or industry groups. It pays to think about these audiences outside of a crisis and proactively compile a comprehensive list of stakeholders you need to consider in different scenarios.

Know Your Team, and Structure Accordingly: Prepare *before* a crisis. Observe and understand the skills of the communicators on your team, or on other teams across your organization, assess where development needs to occur and invest in training courses where necessary. Think about team members who possess graphic design skills, mastery of social media, good relationships with the traditional media, and other skillsets. Utilize crisis activities such as tabletop planning exercises and scenarios to prepare your teams and to examine areas for reinforcement, along with assessing your team's readiness for a large-scale emergency situation. And think about where you may need to supplement these skillsets either during the hiring process or with consulting resources.

Filling the Gaps: Understand and plan where consultants and experts are necessary and can be incorporated into a situation when extra support is needed. For the purposes of the communications work in the Merrimack Valley, it would have been useful to have had more pre-existing relationships with crisis communications consulting teams who shared the same values as our company. We managed to overcome many challenges with the team we eventually built, though it took precious time. The main consulting firm we used had a Boston presence along with strong Massachusetts legislative capabilities, but oftentimes, we found we were missing a true local connection. The residents of the city of Lawrence, while only about 30 miles from Boston, have vastly different sensibilities than true Bostonians, and those differences often presented challenges. While those challenges were not insurmountable, had we developed relationships with consultancy firms ahead of time, we may have avoided some of our earlier missteps.

For your own purposes, while it may not be financially feasible to have a crisis communications consultant on retainer, it may be beneficial to have an expert assess your current crisis communications plan, or help you build a framework for one before a crisis occurs. Alternately, many of the firms that your organization may use for other types of consulting work may have a crisis communications or risk management arm. This could prove valuable for financial purposes, for example, if you need to set up a consultant in your supplier or accounting systems quickly in case of an emergency situation. No matter your organization size, you can start to do some research into crisis communications consultants now who can provide you with the necessary tools to deal with a crisis should one occur in the future. The point is, don't wait. Talk to your leadership about the importance of preparation and proceed according to your own individual circumstances. In the Merrimack Valley, we found ourselves somewhat hindered by the lack of planning and prior relationships.

CHAPTER 9

IT'S ALL SOCIAL

During the Merrimack Valley crisis and the ensuing restoration effort, social media played a large role in the company's public interactions. As a natural gas distribution company, interaction on social media was a small piece of the overall communications strategy. Think about your own experiences in dealing with your utility companies. Typically, if you are contacted by a utility, it's for a service or a billing issue. In 2018, the Columbia companies didn't have a significant following on any of their social media channels and didn't devote significant time to social media beyond routine posting and monitoring.

As a result, the majority of the company's day-to-day social media interactions consisted of posts that highlighted natural gas safety and community engagement activities or philanthropic efforts. In the event of a natural gas outage, our communications professionals posted the location of the outage and the timeline for repairs, along with any additional details such as location of warming shelters if the weather was cold, or the relight process in the case that a customer may not be home.

But in the Merrimack Valley, much of the crisis, as well as communication about the crisis, was playing out on social media channels. Not only was information about the crisis constantly shared amongst the community, but the Columbia Gas and NiSource channels were being used as a tool for customer service at a rate and volume for which we were not prepared. The affected public used the channels (mainly Facebook and Twitter) to ask questions, demand answers and to alert others to potential situations in the community.

Local, state and federal government and public officials used social media channels to relay information to affected residents and, at times, also demand answers from the company. While these unofficial demands for answers were not formal requests for information, the company still needed to provide a response. Speaking for myself, we also had a responsibility to respond to incorrect information where it was shared and identified, whether or not we were tagged in the post.

Social media presented a challenge for the company early on. Because of our limited use of social channels as proactive tools, we didn't have the resources to devote the right level of attention to the fast-paced spread of information. For example, on September 13, immediately following the explosions, information was shared at lightning speed. This included not only news and speculation about the event itself, but also individual concerns from residents of the Andover, Lawrence and North Andover communities. While NiSource and CMA were struggling to produce a simple media statement, the social media superhighway of information was passing us by. It wasn't that we were ignoring the conversation—we simply couldn't keep up.

Additionally, with the attention of the communications team diverted to addressing the concerns of the communities and other important stakeholders, we were not thinking about the past five posts that had been uploaded to the Columbia Gas of Massachusetts social media channels. When alerted to the fact that the most recent post (prior to the incident) was coverage of an award extolling CMA's commitment to safety, we immediately removed the post. It wasn't that the company wasn't committed to safety—far from it. But in the wake of the events of September 13, these types of self-congratulatory posts were tone deaf at best.

Once the communications team was more firmly established, we quickly recognized that we needed a team dedicated to social media response and pivoted to make this happen. While social media response is never an exact science and is often at the whim of the general public at any given moment, the Merrimack Valley accident changed the way the company as a whole viewed these channels thereafter.

CRO Albanese, a savvy user of social media himself, recognized the importance of information-gathering through Facebook and Twitter. He understood that customers were sharing information about the overall project that could be useful to him and his leadership team, both from a project completion standpoint and a communications standpoint.

The CRO brought in his own team of consultants to consistently monitor social media, not for the purpose of response, but for business intelligence. He paired this group with the zone commanders out in the field to solve problems that weren't necessarily being reported through traditional channels.

The company had done a good job of proactively educating employees on its social media policy, and that prior education paid off in the Merrimack Valley. With information and speculation flowing freely on social channels, this situation may have been the perfect scenario for well-meaning employees to try to help by answering individual posts or tweets, or defend the company's response in the face of criticism. But the company encountered very little self-directed engagement on the part of the employees, partly due to the scope of the event itself, but also as a result of the education around its social media policy. Employees knew not to wade into those waters, which could become extremely deep, very quickly.

It was also clear that we needed the right people using the right tone to participate in those interactions. Understandably, the social media engagement from the community was not always polite and friendly. The responding employees needed to understand that all reaction and response must be communicated with honesty, transparency and compassion, by someone with a thick skin. While most of the company's social media representatives responded in a positive manner, there were some instances where the relentless pressure and open hostility did affect a few employees. In those cases, the company brought in others to take over the task of social media monitoring and reaction.

Social media users expected immediate answers to inquiries even when there were not always readily available answers to questions. Questions coming in through the channels often involved complex information that needed to be researched before a communications team member could report back. There were times when these answers took hours to track down. In some cases, as a result of an inquiry, new processes needed to be put into place. In those instances, our employees needed to ask for patience from a public whose patience had worn thin.

Inquiries came in 24/7 and the team did its best to respond as quickly as possible. Even without immediate answers, customers sometimes just appreciated a human response and assurance that the issue was being addressed until a direct answer could be provided.

Because of the visibility of social media, the speed with which users can engage, and the fact that companies can respond on a whim, there were instances of company executives wanting to respond to posts that were simply distractions. Baseless accusations and falsehoods are easy to spread on social media, and response to each unfounded charge or comment is a diversion and can result in a waste of time and resources.

Similarly, the company saw a marked increase in the use of social media to drive the amplification of platforms that were indirectly related to the pipeline accident in the Merrimack Valley. For example, actors who were campaigning to stop further pipeline expansion in the northeast seized on this incident to illustrate their messaging. It was important for the company to recognize that while we may have been tagged in these posts, we did not always need to *respond* to these posts.

In addition to business intelligence and customer service, the team employed a strategy to communicate important updates to the communities through social channels. Key messaging regarding the Gas Ready and House Ready plans, relight work, and other critical announcements were communicated through Facebook and Twitter in addition to other communications channels such as newsletters, customer emails, brochures, community-specific channels, advertising and word-of-mouth methods through the zone commanders.

While all tactics involved in the communications strategy were important, it was also important to continue to remind the dedicated social media team that social media could not be our *only* source of response. There are still plenty of members of the public who don't use social media for a variety of reasons. In the Merrimack Valley, there were many affected residents who didn't have access to a computer, let alone social media channels. Like every other strategy, all factors must be taken into consideration to reach the maximum number of customers or stakeholders. Social media is only one part of the puzzle.

And just like any other communications content that was produced, content of social posts needed to be translated and then approved by communications and project leadership along with internal and external legal counsel and stakeholders from the municipalities and state government. It became imperative to implement a process and timeline for the creation of social media content that also considered the review process and posting schedule. Following is an example of a similar high-level process that was used for content creation, review and posting.

Proactive Social Media Process Flow
Social Customer Care and emergent issues will be addressed by the Social Customer Care Team

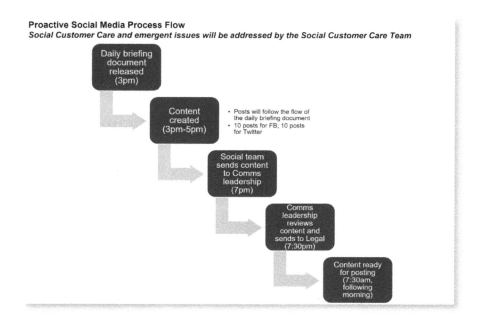

KEY TAKEAWAYS

(Lessons Learned)

A Major Social Element: Be prepared for social media to become a key factor in your crisis communications response. In fact, there may be situations where social media becomes the reason for the crisis. Don't wait for a crisis to occur before you have a social media response plan in place. As you think about crisis communications planning, ensure you're incorporating social media response strategies (both proactive and reactive) to avoid playing catch-up when the time comes.

If your company uses social media on a limited basis during normal business operations, make sure your executive team understands the implications of a fast-moving story in the world of online information. Social media is now inexorably linked to traditional news cycles and absolutely cannot be avoided during a crisis, or even during a time of increased public attention.

It's Not All Bad: Although the threat of a post or a story going viral can cause fear even in the most seasoned company leaders, social media has some tremendous benefits, including the ability to immediately gauge the impact of a story on branding or reputation, as well as providing an opportunity to quickly discern the public call to action.

Social media can also be invaluable in finding information about the company you might not otherwise have. Just as the CRO realized community members were engaging in dialogue that could benefit the overall project, your social media followers could be sharing invaluable information that could help you improve performance inside or outside of a crisis situation. Consider ways to augment your existing social media team so they have the tools and resources to use channels to gather business intelligence.

Put the Shoe on the Other Foot: Put yourself in your customers' position and communicate transparently and compassionately. Social media is largely faceless. Unlike a phone call, it can be easy to forget there is a human at the other end of the keyboard. Ensure your employees are trained in the art of response before assigning them customer service responsibilities through social media channels. In a crisis situation, the interaction may likely start off "hot," and if your employees aren't able to keep their cool, the interaction may do more damage than good. As we discussed in the last chapter, don't be afraid to make an assignment change if you feel you don't have the right people responding directly to customers.

It Can Get Noisy: Don't lose sight of your mission in the face of social media distractions. In the middle of a crisis, you will have legitimate customers or stakeholders asking valid questions. You may also find outsiders who are trying to highjack and take advantage of the situation for their own gain or because of their own agendas. Avoid the temptation to dedicate time, resources and energy to these disruptive posters and detractors. Remind your executive team of the mission at hand when it comes to social media presence and response.

Follow the Rules: Ensure that employees know and understand your social media policies. And if you don't have policies regarding social media interaction, take the time to develop them. As an employee, it can be tempting to jump in and defend the company, especially if the company isn't doing anything to defend itself. But interactions on social media can spiral quickly, and employees should not place their own reputations at risk by jumping in too quickly. Additionally, employees are not meant to become company spokespeople. After all, that's why communications departments exist. It is imperative that you educate your employees regarding reputation management, both the reputation of the company and their own reputations.

A Strategy That Lives On: Pay attention to your social media strategy throughout the life of the crisis. It can be draining, time consuming and daunting, but social media is an extremely effective communications tool if you're using it correctly. Social media is a way to service your customers in real time, and by managing your channels, you can benefit your entire customer base. Don't abandon your users after a few token update posts. Take the time to actively monitor these avenues for issues, and work to solve the problems that come to your attention through your social channels.

Once you're out of crisis response mode, think about the way you use your social media channels. Is your social media strategy doing all it can for you? Are you leaving brand image on the table by ignoring this form of communication? For all the old school communicators out there, this may be a good place to engage fresh voices and ideas on the subject.

CHAPTER 10

EXPECT THE
UNEXPECTED

As the company continued through the bulk of the restoration work—replacing over 45 miles of pipeline and replacing and reinstalling thousands of natural gas appliances—countless unpredictable issues emerged. We will go through some of these unexpected occurrences here, regarding the effect that these issues had on the communications process and the need for flexibility in communications across the communities. Note that these issues appeared throughout the life of the restoration process.

The task of replacing 45 miles of pipeline across three communities caused its own unique communications challenges. Thousands of construction contractors worked on the streets of North Andover, Lawrence and Andover. While this pipeline replacement work was being coordinated and organized by zone, construction crews attempted to finish this work as quickly as possible so that appliances could be reconnected before winter weather hit. The amount of work in the concentrated area south of the Merrimack River caused massive traffic problems in and around the three towns.

The company made an effort to communicate the Gas Ready work by posting a schedule on its website and on an interactive map that had been unveiled for affected residents; however, information technology (IT) issues hampered the interactive map's effectiveness from the start, and frequent shifts in the crews' work affected the schedule's predictably. Instead, the team relied on the zone commanders, targeted communications, social media, public officials and emergency responders to communicate with community members regarding timelines.

While the pipeline replacement work was progressing rapidly, the contractor who had been hired to coordinate the appliance replacement and associated behind-the-meter work struggled to meet its deadlines.

A warehouse in nearby Methuen, Massachusetts, was filled with thousands of pieces of inventory—gas dryers, ranges and furnace/boiler combinations—in a variety of models and finishes, which were ready to be installed quickly. But when assessors visited the homes to evaluate their readiness for appliance installation, in many cases they found extremely aged residential infrastructure that required extensive repair and construction work before appliances could be replaced. In some cases, stairs needed to be built to reach basements where damaged natural gas appliances were located.

Additionally, the company had worked with the state of Massachusetts to expedite the mandated permitting process, but the number of plumbers brought in to perform the final inspection and permitting work fell short of the necessary numbers to complete the process.

As the pace of the pipeline replacement work increased, the number of appliances being replaced fell behind. In the command center, many employees privately worried about the possibility the company might miss the previously communicated November 19 deadline for project completion.

I must stress that a delay had not been stated or confirmed by any project leadership team member, but it was clear from the amount of work and the challenges encountered that the possibility of a delay existed.

From a communications perspective, we were especially worried because the team knew a delay would be incredibly detrimental to both the ongoing project and our tenuous reputation with our customers. The leadership team had given multiple public interviews expressing optimism in this date—a target that was as important in terms of winter weather as it was to ensure families were home and together for the holiday season. Customers were tired of the delays and the wait for service restoration, and employees and contractors of Columbia Gas and NiSource wanted to return customers to their homes and businesses nearly as much as customers wanted to be home.

Separately, a partnership between the office of the governor, the Massachusetts Emergency Management Agency (MEMA) and Columbia Gas had been put in place to ensure that enough temporary housing was available for all affected residents. While the most severely impacted residents were being temporarily housed in hotel rooms around the area, the company had no formal way of tracking them and no longer-term plan for housing assistance and needs.

At the direction of the governor's administration, MEMA worked with Columbia Gas to institute a temporary housing program that included hotel rooms, apartments and travel trailers. In addition, a congregate shelter was established as an alternative option for affected residents and families.

While all parties were committed to the temporary housing program, there were challenges with the booking system. At the outset, the Columbia Gas claims process didn't have the resources required to adequately book residents and families into the hotel rooms, causing confusion and delays. To address this issue, the company brought in a hospitality vendor company who had reservation and booking capabilities. The company also enlisted the help of additional employees to manage the temporary housing process from the company's end, improving the process for residents.

An aerial view of an RV park in Lawrence, Massachusetts, November 2018. Photo credit: NiSource

Travel trailers, or recreational vehicles (RVs), were also housed at five sites around the Lawrence, Andover and North Andover areas. While these sites were not suitable for persons with disabilities or toddlers, many families found this option desirable for many reasons. Unlike a hotel room or an apartment, which may have been as far as 30 miles away, the travel trailer sites were closer to home. For people who had to commute to work or send children to local schools, proximity to jobs and community resources was important. Additionally, residents of these RV parks were grouped with other people from their towns who were all enduring the same situation. There was a sense of comradery and shared experience in these temporary communities. Finally, these residents had immediate access to information that may have taken longer to reach the segregated hotel rooms around the area. For example, zone commanders regularly visited the RV parks to provide information, respond to residents' needs and report back to the command center.

For those residents who had elderly family members or very small children, a number of apartments in the area were also reserved. These apartments were particularly suitable for larger families or those requiring special accommodations.

In addition to the early issues in the reservation process, the matter of pet accommodation proved to be an unanticipated challenge. A second challenge was ensuring that important messaging about the project was relayed to people utilizing the temporary housing program. Those individuals living temporarily in apartments and hotel rooms were spread over a large area, and it was imperative the company track these locations closely so updates could be delivered in a timely manner. A third challenge included weatherization of the travel trailers in the case of cold winter weather, which we will discuss more in-depth in a subsequent chapter.

At its peak, the temporary housing program housed more than 2,000 families and 8,000 individuals, making this type of program the largest in the history of the state of Massachusetts.[34]

An additional challenge encountered by the project, exacerbated by the expanding timeframe for replacement of appliances, came in the form of relationships between property owners and tenants in the area. While these issues were legal in nature and outside the scope of Columbia Gas's ability to resolve them, the team received dozens of inquiries from tenants, nervous

---

34 For more information on the Columbia Gas Temporary Housing Program visit the "*Merrimack Valley Natural Gas Explosions After Action Report, September 13 - December 16, 2018,*" https://www.mass.gov/doc/merrimack-valley-natural-gas-explosions-after-action-report/download Pages 73-91. An article from the Eagle Tribune newspaper published on October 8, 2018, also presents a snapshot of the housing situation at the moment in time: https://www.eagletribune.com/news/merrimack_valley/hotels-fill-trailers-arrive-shelter-opens-under-gas-housing-plan/article_7d310cdd-77d1-5371-ae90-fd38d0c11372.html.

about the future of their permanent housing situation. For example, tenants didn't know if property owners would continue to honor their leases or rental agreements that had been instituted before the accident. These inquiries were received through multiple channels including emails, social media, phone calls to the call center, and through zone commanders and public officials. Property owners were also impatient, as they were losing rental income from units that were inhabitable. The Massachusetts attorney general was on hand to assist with inquiries about disputes between property owners and tenants.

The company also encountered many situations where businesses had existed without proper licensing and business registration, as well as undocumented and formalized landlord/tenant arrangements. It was extremely difficult for CMA, NiSource or our claims representatives to help support customers who may not have been paying business taxes or had no legal certification and/or claims to their rental properties. And while it may have been outside the scope of Columbia Gas or NiSource to mediate these types of undocumented relationships, affected customers argued that they would not have been in the situations in which they found themselves if the events of September 13 had not occurred.

Meanwhile, the business community was facing its own unique challenges. Because of the nature of business needs, particularly in the cases of restaurants, their operations needed specialty natural gas equipment not stocked in the appliance warehouse in Methuen. Company leaders were acutely aware that not only were businesses unable to produce revenue, these businesses were unable to pay workers, affecting people who had not been directly impacted by the gas accident. As a result, the CRO and leadership team brought in a special project manager and project team and instituted "Operation Back to Business" to accelerate the process of both pipeline and appliance replacement to these commercial operations.

We developed specialized communications for this group of customers and held a dedicated town hall with the affected business owners. The company formed a tiger team of project managers, and each business was assigned a contact person with whom the business could communicate on a regular basis throughout the restoration process. While the Back to Business effort was not without its own challenges, the recognition of individual needs of businesses in the three communities helped to facilitate the process of restoring service.

In addition to the societal challenges that were continuously uncovered, the company experienced logistical challenges regarding its own billing systems, in that the systems could not be immediately halted and then reinstituted with new schedules and in new configurations. Many of the customers who may have had gas service interrupted in mid-September and were subsequently found to have been connected to an unaffected gas distribution system disputed paying for gas service for the length of time that their service had been interrupted. While the company put into place a system to restart the billing cycles for these customers, it was not perfect, and communication to customers about what to expect was flawed, as most of the restoration team's attention was still on the ongoing crisis. This proved to be a critical communications misstep at the end of the restoration period and caused unnecessary alarm and negative media attention.

These are just a few examples of the countless challenges encountered by the restoration project, and each challenge required a public response and communication to multiple stakeholders. But because of the legal sensitivities surrounding both the project and the issues, as well as the public scrutiny and the ongoing NTSB investigation, every piece of communications material produced needed to undergo a rigorous review process. Not only did the company's legal team need to review all content, but outside legal counsel, project managers, restoration team executive leadership, public officials from the city and towns, the attorney general's office, and the governor's office, also needed to review all material.

Adhering to this necessary and rigorous review cycle involving the main stakeholders—the affected customers—was challenging for the communications team. We worked with our internal group of legal counsel, one of whom was always on call. That legal representative facilitated review with the company's outside counsel. Following legal review, for version control, either my counterpart or I then initiated the stakeholder review process for each piece of communications content. This could be frustrating because of the considerable number of participants in the review cycle. In an attempt to expedite the review process, we were sure to give a deadline by which review was necessary, and we held fast to the premise that if review or comment was not received by that time, the document would be finalized and sent for printing and/or distribution. Of course, there were times when the commitment to these deadlines needed to be relaxed, and we were flexible. But without deadlines, the documents would never have made it out the door. The following process flow is an example of a similar communications review process that was used for weekly customer newsletters.

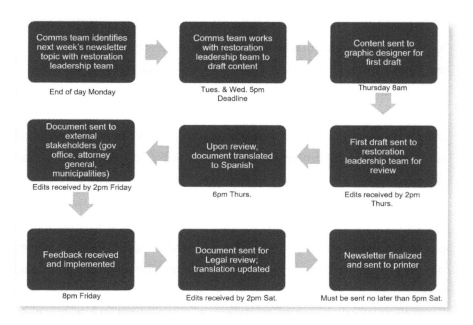

As multiple challenges faced the company throughout the course of the restoration process, it became imperative that members of the communications team be included in nearly every conversation. It was important for us to understand the details and nuances of each of those conversations because of the need to communicate clearly and quickly with large and varying audiences under strict review processes.

KEY TAKEAWAYS
(Lessons Learned)

The Crisis within a Crisis: Every challenge the team encountered required a full-scale communications plan, including internal communications (web updates and legal and executive interface), public relations mitigation, external affairs and community outreach, targeted customer communications and, in some cases, advertising opportunities to reach the largest audience. It was extremely difficult to execute on the established communications plan that focused on the mission in front of us when challenges and diversions occurred nearly every day. I've talked about the need for flexibility, but it is also crucial to be able to move quickly, to pivot immediately and most importantly, to give yourselves and your teams the grace to be less than perfect.

In any communications effort, it's important to adhere to a review process, and this becomes even more critical in a crisis. While I have always been a process-driven communicator, I learned from this situation that those review cycles that you may deem unnecessary in normal operations can save hours of time in a crisis. Don't be afraid to enforce process, even when they may frustrate others. Likewise, don't be afraid to adjust processes when those processes are inefficient or just don't make sense.

Get Out of Your Lane: In a large crisis situation, expect to veer far outside of your normal lane of operation. In normal business operations, communications teams may be included as a part of the process, but a communications professional will not typically be asked to make business decisions. In a crisis, many times, communication *is* the business decision.

It is imperative that you become comfortable with speaking up when something doesn't make sense. There were many times that the communications team identified business process issues and suggested process improvements simply because we were responsible for creating the communications materials outlining or explaining that process. In a crisis, your input can influence a matter of public reputation, so don't avoid speaking out about responsibilities you feel are outside the scope of your job or rocking the boat a bit to make improvements.

Managing Complexity: In situations involving intricate legal matters, try to set up a manageable review cycle ahead of time. We discussed earlier the importance of establishing a relationship with your legal representatives before a crisis occurs. In the case of a complex emergency situation, ensure that you're communicating regularly and transparently with your legal counsel and other interested parties to protect yourself and the company, as well as ensuring your stakeholders are getting the information they need the most. While the review cycle was a challenge, it allowed for differing perspectives to be offered, which nearly always benefited the customers in the end.

Develop a Thick Skin: Communications is often the end of the line, and while as a communicator you may not have overall responsibility for the entire project, when things go wrong, "communication" will often be cited as the reason. You may decry this as unfair, but it's the nature of the job. There are plenty of instances where you will need to take your lumps and move on, because like everyone else, you are not perfect, and you will not catch every detail of every process. A crisis cannot be predicted, and there is no overall blueprint for every emergency situation. Flexibility is important. Make process improvements where necessary, do your best and be gentle with yourself, even when the rest of the world is tough on you.

CHAPTER 11

A VICTORY AND A MAJOR SETBACK

Despite the astounding progress made in replacing 45 miles of pipeline in the Merrimack Valley, by the last week in October, it was clear that a new strategy was necessary for the replacement of appliances for the affected customers. The external team that had been hired to perform all of the "behind the meter" work simply did not have the workforce and other resources necessary to tackle a job as complex as this one. Some of the obstacles the team encountered included the discovery of asbestos and lead paint in a significant number of homes, in addition to other severe code violations, all of which needed to be mitigated before inspectors could sign off on work. In some cases, the company needed to make major structural upgrades to affected homes before the appliance replacement could even begin.

On Friday, October 26, 2018, the CRO was joined by senior leadership from NiSource, the governor's office, and city and town officials at a press conference to announce that the timeline for the restoration of gas service was being updated from the original November 19 date to "no later than December 16, 2018." It was a blow to the project, but more importantly, it was a blow to the hopes of the affected residents in the Merrimack Valley. The company made this disappointing announcement on October 26, 44 days since residents last had gas service, and in many cases, had been back to their homes. The delay meant there was a good chance that many residents would not have gas service restored before the Thanksgiving holiday, though the company and the restoration team continued to pledge to get people back into their homes as quickly as possible.

In the meantime, to expedite the appliance work, the team shifted to a strategy involving the repair of furnaces or boilers, where it was safe to do so, with a guarantee that the team would be back to replace those repaired appliances the following spring. Internally, the restoration leadership team coined this phrase "Operation Rapid Relight." In addition to the option to repair rather than replace a furnace or boiler, the team prioritized the replacement or repair of furnaces or boilers over other natural gas appliances to expedite customers' return to their homes. Replacement of dryers and stoves was a secondary task that would follow the same or next day.

The restoration team also focused heavily on the self-mitigation option, encouraging affected residents to replace their own appliances through the claims process, independent of Columbia Gas contractors, where they had the means to take this action. By encouraging this option for as many customers as possible, and providing targeted support for those customers who had decided to self-mitigate, the restoration leadership team was able to make resources available to focus more heavily on those customers who did not have the option or the means to self-mitigate.

To further expedite the volume of House Ready work that needed to take place, the CRO announced that the restoration leadership team would utilize three additional contractors along with hundreds more plumbers and gas fitters, in addition to the existing appliance replacement contractor.

From a communications standpoint, this shift in strategy required the team to think through ways to communicate these changes to the affected public. Beginning October 27, the restoration leadership team held a series of three town halls—one each in Lawrence, North Andover and Andover. These town halls were open to both the public and the media, with a press gaggle provided immediately following the events, where question-and-answer sessions were limited to affected customers, residents and community members.

While the restoration team took its share of criticism from the public about the shift in direction, the town hall format was helpful in allowing project leaders to hear directly from customers and community members, as well providing a central location for affected residents to receive answers to questions. The sessions included opening remarks from the project leadership and featured separate private areas for claims, pipeline safety information, and questions about construction and appliance replacement. The company also provided dedicated customer care specialists available to answer any questions about high-level project details.

Restoration and Recovery leaders address residents in affected communities during a town hall discussion. Photo credit: NiSource

The customers who attended the town halls, and displayed emotion as they expressed their fears and uncertainty about the future, reminded the entire project leadership team why we were putting in 14-hour days and—in many cases—living hours away from our families for weeks at a time.

In addition to the town halls, the team focused on updating communications channels to supplement the website, social media posts and press releases/conferences. The company instituted a renewed focus on the interactive map which reflected the updated House Ready schedule. The communications team also placed renewed emphasis on the 72-hour schedule on its website, ensuring it was updated to the best of the team's ability each night. A weekly newsletter[35] was created for all affected residents and posted on the company's website, as well as mailed to either customers' home addresses or temporary housing addresses.

---

35   An example of a past Merrimack Valley Restoration newsletter can be found by visiting: https://www.columbiagas.com/docs/librariesprovider3/greater-lawrence/ weekly-newsletter---11-19-18.pdf?sfvrsn=4.

With the delay of the overall project schedule, it was also imperative that the company continue to encourage affected residents to continue to explore alternative housing arrangements with the approaching onset of cold weather.

While this announcement was unwelcome, there was some good news to be shared. On October 30, the company announced the completion of the gas pipeline construction project, which included the installation of 43.5 miles of gas main lines, 5,086 service lines, and the requalification of over 12 miles of main line polyethylene pipe, which included enhanced safety features such as emergency flow valves.[36] The pipeline construction was completed three weeks ahead of schedule, which was a major industry accomplishment. Even so, residents who could not return to their homes, or to businesses still unable to open, were less than impressed with the achievement. They just wanted the ordeal to be over.

KEY TAKEAWAYS
(Lessons Learned)

Transparency is Always the Right Decision... even if people don't like what you have to say. While the team communicated project updates as soon as it became clear that the original deadline would slip, there was a sense from the community that the project leadership knew this information long before they told the public. This was not the case, and the restoration leadership team was in constant contact with the city and town officials, as well as state officials. While we all recognized that an

---

36   https://www.prnewswire.com/news-releases/columbia-gas-completes-gas-pipeline-construction-project-now-fully-focused-on-in-home-work-300740339.html

announcement of a delay would not be well received, it was imperative that affected residents understand how the changing timeline may alter their plans, especially with the approach of winter weather. The company took its lumps in the press and in a public forum, but the announcement in late October gave the communities time to plan for a delay and enhance public resources. It also gave frustrated residents the opportunity to plan beyond the Thanksgiving holiday.

As a communicator, if you find yourself in a situation during which a company executive or other leader advocates for holding back information, no matter how well-intentioned their withholding may be, it should be your duty to remind him or her of both the ethical obligation to provide information as well as the negative impacts that may be incurred by a perceived cover-up or smokescreen. As the company learned in the very early days of the Merrimack Valley crisis, sharing information, no matter how scant or disappointing, is highly preferable to saying nothing at all.

Keep It in Perspective: During a crisis, your team should be able to pivot and respond quickly, especially in the face of unwelcome news. In a crisis as large and complex as this one, details shifted daily. But, even for a team of people who had become somewhat accustomed to the changing nature of the project, this acknowledgement of a delay in the project was a larger shift than the other delays had been. This shift affected not only communications plans, but it also affected lives and was a major setback.

While we've discussed the need to be flexible in the face of changing conditions, it also helps to keep in mind a constant and tangible objective to ground you in the face of upheavals and changes. In our case, business owners and residents gave direct feedback, and this was helpful to keep the situation in perspective. A crisis isn't a crisis unless someone is impacted. Remind yourself early and often about the impacted parties and use the effects of those impacts to guide your way through intricate processes, procedures and changes. In other words, keep the "why" or your motivations for your continued participation in mind at all times.

The Value of a Public Forum: Town hall meetings, or other public forums, are effective venues for engaging with the public and sharing information. Columbia Gas and the restoration team held three total sessions of town hall meetings throughout the restoration project—nine meetings in total—and each of these sessions was valuable in its own way. These sessions gave residents the chance to vent and communicate their own stories, which in many cases were shared by project leadership in other forums. For the restoration leadership team, it gave a face to the affected customers, and it reminded all the workers who attended the town hall sessions of the purpose of our mission. For the affected residents, it personalized the work being done and helped to illustrate that while there was a corporation on the other end of the work taking place in the street and in homes, there were also real people making the best decisions they could to give customers back some sense of normalcy.

Looking back, I wish we'd held town halls earlier than we did. It would have been helpful to allow residents a public forum to express their frustrations and ask questions earlier than 44 days into the crisis. It would have also allowed the team a chance to gather critical feedback about the progress on the ground as we adjusted processes and procedures.

A town hall meeting does not need to be a dedicated and standalone event. This type of meeting can be held in conjunction with existing township or city meetings, with the cooperation of municipal leaders. Nor does it need to be an elaborate display. If it is necessary for your team to address a targeted group of people, a town hall or an open house forum, during which the public is strategically separated into more manageable groups, may be a great option for a focused communications channel.

Take Good News Where You Can Get It: The positive news of a record-breaking pipeline replacement project was overshadowed by the unwelcome announcement of the overall project delay, but it's still important to communicate (and celebrate) progress where you can. The schedule changes didn't stop us from letting customers know, through press releases, website and social media updates, that the pipeline replacement work was finished. It may have been underappreciated at the time, but it was a significant milestone in gas restoration, and it marked the major accomplishment of a new and safe natural gas system that was built to last for decades to come. And even if residents didn't celebrate the construction feat that had taken place, industry publications were interested in discussing how the project was managed and implemented.

From a communications perspective, even in the midst of a crisis, it's important to consider differing audiences. There are often indirect or secondary audiences who may appreciate the complexities of a project. While these audiences are not your number one priority, they may be important to your company at a later date, and they shouldn't be forgotten.

Consistency Is Key: We've discussed this previously, but it bears repeating: the communications team is (or should be) involved in every aspect of a crisis. From speechwriting, talking points and town hall planning and execution, to social media updates, to website content, press releases and follow-up statements, messaging must be consistent. A good incident commander or project leader will recognize this need, but if he/she does not, it's up to you and your team to insert yourselves into the situation.

CHAPTER 12

OPERATION
DEEP FREEZE

n the first week of November 2018, the temperature highs were in the fifties. By the second week, high temperatures had fallen into the 40s with lows in the low 30s. By the third week, forecasters were predicting that the high temperatures would fall into the 20s and teens. With the pipeline replacement work completed and three new contractors on board, the team started to make progress in restoring gas service to customers' homes. But work wasn't progressing quickly enough to keep up with Mother Nature. The restoration team knew that a separate plan was needed specifically to address the upcoming winter weather.

The CRO and his team assessed the number of individuals and families who were taking advantage of temporary housing arrangements. On November 1, 2018, a little over 7,000 individuals were living in either a hotel room, RV or an apartment.[37]

In addition to residents who had not yet had heat and hot water restored, a second group of residents that worried the restoration team were the "self-mitigators"—those customers who were replacing their own appliances through the claims process—over whom the project had no influence with progress. In response, the leadership team deployed the zone commanders who went door-to-door to make personal contact with affected residents in the areas. While safety and warmth of the residents was the primary concern, there were additional worries such as burst pipes and subsequent water damage in the homes of those residents who were already living in temporary housing.

The communications team quickly drafted a public relations campaign to reach as many residents as possible with critical information. This campaign

37   https://www.cityoflawrence.com/718/Lawrence-Gas-Emergency Daily Coordination
Call briefing documents for the month of November.

utilized social media posts encouraging residents to check on their vulnerable neighbors and to call to arrange for temporary housing. English and Spanish radio advertisements were employed to communicate the details of temporary housing reservations and arrangements and targeted safety text messaging to affected residents. We also continued to encourage consideration of alternative living arrangements (hotels, RVs, temporary apartments) in the newly created weekly newsletter. Additionally, we distributed to all temporary housing sites flyers that warned residents of the possibility of freezing pipes in their uninhabited homes. The team also reached out to local and metropolitan media contacts to help us spread the message to affected residents.

Via customer email, we focused the messaging on checking on friends and neighbors often, in particular the elderly population and those residents with young children who may be without heat or hot water. We also sent emails with more comprehensive information on pipes which were more at risk of freezing, and instructions on how to protect pipes, especially when temperatures were forecasted to drop below freezing for multiple consecutive days.

The restoration leadership team worked with elected officials and emergency response personnel in Lawrence, Andover and North Andover to augment these messages, and the municipalities had plans in place to gain entry to customers' homes in the event of an emergency. Additionally, our community relations team worked with local social services agencies within the towns and cities to ensure that the municipalities had the necessary resources should the weather cause the need for additional shelter, winter clothing or other temporary heating equipment.

While we felt as though we had done as much as possible to prepare residents for the cold weather ahead, we could do nothing but wait and respond as Mother Nature entered the Northeast at full force. One thing we had not anticipated was the effect of the Massachusetts winter on the travel trailers which were occupied by affected residents.

The team quickly discovered that the travel trailers were not winterized, nor were they built to withstand New England winter conditions. According to the "Merrimack Valley Natural Gas Explosions After Action Report" published by the MEMA, each trailer needed to be covered in thick insulating foam, and heated lines needed to be installed under every trailer to guarantee that the underside of the RVs did not freeze and that maintenance valves could be accessed and operated despite the frozen conditions.

Additionally, according to the MEMA report, there were many identified challenges related to travel trailer maintenance. Some of the specific weather-related challenges included:

- Site/trailer maintenance and scheduling of services
- Determination of the roles and responsibilities of hired contractors
- Identification of contracted services and terms of agreement
- Scheduling of twice-daily visits to every trailer to replace an empty propane tank and ensure the second propane tank was utilized for continued heating
- Adequate preparation of trailer sites and trailer units for inclement weather (e.g., removing snow, managing mud and pooling water, insulating units from the cold, servicing frozen unit valves)

Specifically, the challenges around insulating units from the cold, and servicing frozen unit valves, posed challenges for the restoration team as well as concern amongst the temporary residents. To my knowledge, none of the temporary residents needed to be moved from their temporary living locations, and all units were able to be winterized and serviced, but anticipation of the challenges caused by the early inclement weather would have saved the team time, energy and resources.

By November 19, despite the fact the gas service was being restored to customers each day, nearly 1,000 additional individuals were utilizing some type of company-provided temporary housing arrangements (hotels, apartments and travel trailers), bringing the total to approximately 8,000 individuals across the affected area.

KEY TAKEAWAYS
(Lessons Learned)

The Art of Preparing for the Worst-Case Scenario: No matter what secondary situations occur during a crisis, while the events may be outside of your control, the response is completely within your control. Even though the weather was something outside the control of the company, many affected residents thought the company and restoration team should have more adequately prepared for the possibility of an early cold snap. So, while the weather itself certainly wasn't something under the team's control, the response was. The job of the communications team was to deploy the right messaging to the most appropriate audiences as nimbly as possible, using the channels identified for each audience. By this time, the team had identified a review process for external communication materials, so we were able to deploy messaging quickly.

Though many parties (including MEMA, the municipalities, and state government officials) were involved in responding to the colder-than-normal temperatures, from a crisis communications perspective the response belonged to Columbia Gas.

All for One, and One for All: While understanding roles and responsibilities is important, members of the team should also be prepared to pitch in wherever necessary to get the job done. While attempting to find an answer to a question pertaining to temporary housing, I made a phone call to Mike Davidson, a fellow executive from Columbia Gas of Pennsylvania, who had also dedicated his time in Massachusetts to lead the company's temporary housing effort. Mike, a tremendous man and an outstanding leader was, at that time, in a U-Haul rental truck filled with foam insulation board, on his way to one of the RV parks to crawl under travel trailers to winterize those vehicles. In his regular day job, Mike led hundreds of employees as he oversaw the operations strategy and execution for two state operating companies. In a crisis, all bets are off. Another senior vice president in the company was frequently seen helping to empty waste from the trailers housing our lavatory trailer.

The command center was the great equalizer when it came to position in the company. You were there to do what the company needed of you at that moment. While many crisis situations will not be this involved, intense, or severe, any crisis response will be helped by the suspension of the ego for the greater good. After all, resolving a crisis has very little to do with you as a person, and much more to do with your affected publics, whether employees, customers/consumers, the general public, or your shareholders or investors.

CHAPTER 13

HAPPY HOLIDAYS

I n late October, when it became clear that Columbia Gas and the Merrimack Valley restoration team would miss the original deadline of November 19, the community relations team began holiday planning discussions with the executive restoration team, Columbia Gas of Massachusetts leadership and municipal leaders. What could the team do to make residents' lives a little more cheerful during a holiday season spent in a hotel room, anonymous apartment, or travel trailer?

The team had originally anticipated that the crisis would be over by Thursday, November 22—Thanksgiving Day. Indeed, by this date, approximately 90 percent of business customers' gas service had been relit and 82 percent of residential customers' service had been restored.

But the team understood that just because a family may have been able to move back home a few days before Thanksgiving, this certainly did not mean they would have the resources to plan a holiday gathering after such a disruptive event in their lives. Furthermore, some families who had decided to self-mitigate may have had their heat restored but were still waiting on their gas stoves and ranges, and they had no way to prepare a meal. Other individuals were deeply traumatized by the situation and still working to return to some sense of normalcy after a deeply distressing event.

Many team members advocated for a simple solution, such as providing gift cards to affected residents who could use the cards to either purchase food or dine out. Community leaders and Columbia Gas executives considered this approach heartless and advocated for a much more personal solution during the holidays. Particularly in the most severely affected Lawrence community, where the Hispanic population focused heavily on family, personal connections, and a deep sense of community, the company and the community wanted to ensure we had done everything possible to help provide a joyful holiday.

These discussions led to a partnership with a local New England eatery to help to institute a Thanksgiving Day plan. Ultimately, the team decided to offer family-sized boxed meals that could be picked up from designated locations in each community, as well as sit-down locations located near RV parks in each community.

Based on an 85 percent acceptance rate, the team estimated that approximately 23,000 meals would be necessary to ensure that every resident had access to a hot meal. But the team needed a way to track the number of boxed meals and sit-down reservations for both food provision and resource purposes. The company implemented a simple reservation system on the Columbia Gas of Massachusetts website, where affected residents could choose their preferred meal and pick-up locations. Affected residents could also call a designated phone number, staffed by customer service representatives, if they did not have access to the website.

Communication to affected residents began on November 7 and channels included the NiSource Merrimack Valley restoration website, which remained the primary source of information throughout the crisis, the weekly newsletter, regular social media updates and traditional media interaction along with community website updates and communication through community social services agencies.

While the reservations were advertised to affected customers in Lawrence, Andover and North Andover, we were aware there was a possibility that others may also attempt to gain access to a meal. The company required identifying information during the reservation process, and we were fortunate that we did not have a large number of individuals outside of the affected area in the Merrimack Valley attempting to circumvent the system and take advantage of the communities' tragic situation.

Volunteers in the Merrimack Valley deliver boxed meals to residents for Thanksgiving at a pickup location in November of 2018. Photo credit: NiSource

One additional challenge to the process was establishing a menu for the day. Traditional Thanksgiving meal choices were offered including turkey, stuffing, mashed potatoes and pumpkin pie. The team was also aware of the cultural differences, particularly in the city of Lawrence, where the population was largely of Dominican ethnicity, so in addition to the traditional

Thanksgiving meal options at the sit-down dinner in Lawrence, an array of Dominican dishes was also offered.

It was a massive undertaking with heavy involvement from Columbia Gas, the Merrimack Valley restoration team, and the communities, who helped to provide coordination support such as meal pick-up locations, traffic directors, tent set-up and decoration, security and volunteers. Restaurant employees worked for two days to prepare approximately 23,000 Thanksgiving Day meals and provided the servers for the sit-down locations. Most of the Columbia Gas of Massachusetts executives spent Thanksgiving Day in the Merrimack Valley, helping to serve meals and interact with community members, and many of the teams' family members flew in to have Thanksgiving in Massachusetts.

In addition to the Thanksgiving Day meal preparation and distribution, Columbia Gas also sponsored the Feaster Five Thanksgiving Day Road Race, held annually in Andover, Massachusetts. Many of the restoration team members, along with Columbia Gas family members, also participated in this race to show their commitment to the community.

KEY TAKEAWAYS
(Lessons Learned)

Extra Effort When It Matters Most: If going above and beyond is going to ease the suffering of the affected audience, consider the extra time, cost and resources as an investment in the well-being of your customers. Most of the time, in crisis communication situations, it pays to make things as simple as possible in terms of time, resources and energy. But in this case, Thanksgiving preparations involved a large logistical undertaking, which included communications, community relations, government affairs, the customer service center, the facilities organization, IT, zone commanders, the temporary housing organization, community leadership, and countless other participants. While handing each resident or family a gift card would have been simpler, early on we determined it was not an option because it did not align with the community/family commitment of this initiative. The Thanksgiving effort, while not a required activity, was one of the best and most rewarding parts of the entire project. Participating in that massive undertaking was a challenge of our making, but it was the right thing to do.

Making Good News: In any crisis, the media has its own motivations. If you can create goodwill (without being insincere or manipulative, and for the good of the people and the cause) and entice the media to report it, this may help you to repair a damaged reputation. One of these motivations is to cover the story; the other is to sell the story. In this case, we knew that the news media would be onsite at the meal pick-up locations and at the sit-down locations, and we had media relations contacts onsite to answer questions and help to facilitate contact with restoration team or Columbia Gas executives. However, the company was also aware the media would be on the lookout for negative stories regarding the timeline for service restoration. By and large, the coverage was positive. An example of the press coverage can be found at https://boston.cbslocal.com/2018/11/21/thanksgiving-mer-rimack-valley-explosions-columbia-gas/. While acknowledging the hardship for residents of the Merrimack Valley, the stories conveyed a tone of blessing and thankfulness, which were definitely themes of the day.

Do Good Anyway: Even when intentions are good, members of the community may not always agree with a company's community involve-ment. Do good anyway. In this case, many members of the communities were unhappy with the Columbia Gas sponsorship of the Feaster Five Road Race. There was a sense that the company was trying to buy goodwill at a time when community members' lives were still in a state of flux and unrest. Despite this criticism, Columbia Gas moved forward with the sponsorship in support of the race itself and the beneficiaries of the organization, as well as demonstrating a true commitment to the Merrimack Valley and its community members. Throughout the crisis situation, many members of the Columbia Gas organization moved to the Merrimack Valley. They established a sense of comradery with the community members and fostered a desire to give back to their temporary hometowns.

The Bright Spots: In a situation filled with angst, anger, frustration and turmoil, find some reasons to celebrate deeper meanings and relationships. The Thanksgiving Day effort was by far one of few examples of optimism in the otherwise intense and focused work of restoring service to customers. Not only did the planning and reservation process proceed relatively smoothly, but the day was also one of celebration and jubilation for community members, volunteers and residents alike. Obviously, affected residents not able to return home would have preferred an uninterrupted holiday, but overall, the day was a success and the efforts to launch such a huge undertaking in a short timeframe paid off.

The holiday celebration in the Merrimack Valley was truly about giving back to the communities who had endured so much since September 13. It's important to recognize that some audiences may perceive your community efforts as insincere or mis-intentioned after an at-fault crisis. Communications should continue to be aware of these potential pitfalls. In this case, the company's motivations were pure, and despite some negative press and doubts regarding our intentions, we decided that serving the community was much more important than the suspicions of those who continued to cast doubt and aspersions. At the end of the day, continue to do what is right, just and ethical, despite any naysayers.

CHAPTER 14

DEALING WITH ANCILLARY ISSUES

While the team continued to focus on restoring gas service to all affected customers, and deal with the effects of the early cold snap across the area, there was still a need to respond to the peripheral challenges that occurred because of the incident and related events.

On November 1, 2018, it was announced that federal authorities had launched a criminal investigation into the company as a result of the events of September 13.[38] Columbia Gas of Massachusetts already faced several lawsuits, an investigation by the National Transportation Safety Board and an investigation by the Massachusetts Department of Public Utilities.

---

38   https://www.wcvb.com/article/gas-company-facing-federal-criminal-investigation-after-explosions-fires/24513587#

At this time, the company became aware that a former Columbia Gas of Massachusetts employee planned to go to the press with allegations that he had repeatedly communicated safety concerns to other CMA employees. He believed that these safety concerns were related to the disaster that occurred on September 13.[39] The reporting of this employee's concern became part of various investigations into the events that led up to the September 13 explosions, as well as the investigations into the company's immediate response to the incident.

On November 15, close to the original target date for service restoration, the NTSB issued a preliminary safety recommendation report, which documented omissions in the engineering plans for work being done on the Columbia Gas pipeline system that led to system overpressurization and the events of September 13. The report included a number of recommendations, some of which NiSource had already implemented. Despite the company's efforts, the story and the issuance of the preliminary report were widely covered in the Boston area.

Columbia Gas and industry leaders testify at a public hearing in Lawrence, Mass., in November 2018. Photo credit: AP Editorial License

---

39   https://www.nbcboston.com/news/local/whistleblower-columbia-gas-cut-corners-prior-to-explosions/130040/

Additionally, six U.S. House and Senate members from Massachusetts and New Hampshire requested that the company participate in a public hearing in Lawrence, where they demanded answers to questions surrounding the events of September 13, and those leading up to it. These government officials also scrutinized and questioned the company's corporate culture.[40] U.S. Senators Ed Markey and Elizabeth Warren both called for measures that included executive and employee accountability for the incident, and greater safety measures for not only the company, but for the industry as a whole. The group of lawmakers also questioned the company's internal procedures which could have prevented or provided a better response to the incident.

Both the then CEO of NiSource and the then president of Columbia Gas of Massachusetts testified on the company's behalf, and assured the lawmakers and the assembled crowd that the company was taking steps to assure another disaster wouldn't happen. This included adopting many of the initial recommendations from the NTSB.

The elected officials also criticized the company for missing its initial goal of restoring gas service to all customers before Thanksgiving, while others suggested the company be sold or disbanded completely.

Leonel Rondon's sister also provided testimony, mourning the loss of her brother and vowing that the family would derive some meaning from the manner of his death by holding the company and the industry accountable.

While all of the described occurrences were directly related to the events of September 13, and were valid complaints and criticism, they were not directly related to the mission of restoring heat and hot water to affected customers and residents in the Merrimack Valley. Public response to each of

---

40 Cooper, Steve. Associated Press. "'No second chances': Mass. politicians say Columbia Gas should close," WHDH, Boston, 26 Nov. 2018, https://whdh.com/news/no-second-chances-mass-politicians-say-columbia-gas-should-close/.

these developments took time and resources away from the more immediate response of service restoration.

There was a tremendous amount of media coverage of these developments. While the company issued responses to each of the media outlets that had reached out for comment, the social media coverage was perhaps more damaging in that the stories invited additional public comment and scrutiny of the company.

For the team on the ground in the Merrimack Valley, the story negatively impacted our ability to use the media to help to distribute vital information to affected customers during the cold winter weather. While the communications team understood the media would notice this information and use it to gain viewers, readers and followers, the restoration project leadership team wanted the communications team to gain better control over the message. After all, several consultants from the Boston area were being employed on the project because of their relationships with the press and external stakeholders. There was a sense that those connections were not being used to their greatest capacity to effectively control the narrative.

The communications team also encountered some pressure from leadership to attempt to turn the story around on social media, which proved to be extremely difficult. The company was now facing the announcement of a criminal investigation, a whistleblower interview combined with continued negative public attention on an event for which the company had already taken full responsibility. In the fast-paced world of social media, the negative attention overwhelmed any positive developments. Additionally, at that point in the project, the efforts of the communications team were focused on customer safety, security and well-being. Many of the emergent ancillary issues dealt with questions around the cause of the accident. As a party to the NTSB's ongoing investigation, there were many allegations to which we were not able to respond.

Additionally, while the team on the ground in Massachusetts was somewhat prepared for the renewed public scrutiny, company employees outside of the Merrimack Valley had not been prepared for the continued public vitriol, nor were they sure how public condemnation would affect the reputation of the NiSource subsidiary companies, should even a minor natural gas incident occur. And more than that, many of the subsidiary companies had been around for generations (with different ownership over the years). There was a familial bond over the name "Columbia Gas," and within the employee population there were numerous examples of multi-generational workers. What happened in Massachusetts had happened to members of a patchwork family, and for the employee population, many workers felt embarrassment and sadness associated with September 13.

Also related, these developing events and national attention caused ripples of unrest throughout the employee-base that not only took attention away from the task at hand, but in some cases, caused members of the team to question the entire mission and their role in it. In my opinion, these distractions were among the most damaging to the mission, because they called into question motivations, professional mistakes and uncertainty about the future of the company itself.

While many of us were participating in the restoration and recovery effort to do our part for the company, and more importantly, restore service to affected customers and residents, it was hard not to question the longer-term goals and potential outcomes related to the events of September 13.

KEY TAKEAWAYS
(Lessons Learned)

Keep Your Eye on the Ball: Distractions will inevitably be introduced into a crisis situation. In this case, the distractions were directly related to the crisis itself. However, the distractions did nothing to change the mission at hand—ensuring affected residents could return home. The challenge facing the entire team was to retain focus on the primary objectives. This was slightly more difficult for the communications team because resources were forced to be diverted in order to publicly respond to the distractions. Even for short periods of time, the loss of resources took a toll on the other team members who needed to pick up extra work.

No matter the nature of your particular crisis situation, be ready for distractions and think about how you will address them ahead of time. It may help to take stock of those who may challenge your industry or your company. As a part of crisis communications planning, a thorough stakeholder analysis should uncover many of these parties and can help to understand what messaging may be necessary in the event a response is warranted. But you should always be prepared for unexpected distractions.

Beware the Shadow of the Subplot: While, in many cases, a response to media inquiries related to distractions is required, social media will take on a life of its own. It often will not benefit the company to respond to every comment on Facebook or Twitter. In crisis situations, it's important to monitor traffic constantly, but the goal should be to manage the message and the situation. Trying to control the message by 1) attacking another party or 2) offering unsolicited defense will continue to feed the beast. In a situation where social media *is* the crisis, companies that do not have specific expertise in crisis social media management may want to consider hiring a firm specializing in social media public relations and listening services. In the Merrimack Valley, the team was using social media primarily as a customer service and intelligence-gathering tool. While none of the comments went "viral" per se, a number of actors were clearly attempting to make that happen, and our solution was to understand and monitor but to ultimately limit engagement.

Coordination with Leaders: Ensure that your senior leadership understands and supports your strategy for dealing with ancillary and distracting developments or stories. Quite a few senior leaders in the Merrimack Valley lobbied for more engagement on social media, and greater involvement in responding to events that were secondary to the goal of restoring heat and hot water. Ultimately, these leaders understood the communications team's reluctance and agreed with the final assessment. But the anticipation of some of these events would have smoothed the way for a more concrete strategy and saved the time of arguing our case.

Keep the Mission in Mind: External parties will have their own personal or professional motivations for reporting on, or even exploiting, a crisis situation. Just as employees or consultants may have primary or secondary goals of personal development or network building, external parties may use a crisis situation to further their own agendas. You may never know what those motivations or agendas are, but what is more significant is resolving the issue at hand and keeping the purpose of the mission top of mind.

CHAPTER 15

A RUSH TO THE FINISH LINE WHERE NO ONE WAS CHEERING

During the critical month of November 2018, in the midst of multiple disruptions including cold weather, outside political influence and the Thanksgiving holiday, the Merrimack Valley restoration team had increased the contractor resources on the ground. This supplemented the original contract resource for the behind-the-meter work with three additional contractors, one of which was dedicated solely to affected business in the Merrimack Valley. Once the leadership team supplemented this important work, the rate of daily relights increased significantly.

For example, on October 25, 2018, the restoration team was only hitting about 10 percent of its overall target. One month later, on November 25, the relight numbers continued their trend of tracking above the plan with the services in over 6,000 homes and businesses restored. And by December 1, the finish line was in sight, with 95 percent of residential meters connected to the natural gas system.[41]

As the project began to wrap up, both contractor and company resources started to extract themselves from the project and make their way back to their own homes before the Christmas holiday. Many affected residents had vacated their temporary housing arrangements, and the travel trailer demobilization process was underway as residents moved back home.

One particular area of concern focused on those residents who had decided to self-mitigate, a process that the company was actively encouraging just a month prior. But with project completion in sight, the restoration team realized we could not claim completion of the project unless 100 percent of residential and business meters had been relit and service had been restored.

The CRO directed the restoration team to deploy existing resources to the special project of guiding self-mitigating residents through the relight process. This meant contacting those residents and encouraging them to accept additional help and resources from Columbia Gas to expedite the process. Some residents welcomed this support; others were not in a rush to restore service for any number of reasons. Some residents had traveled south for the winter months; others were comfortable staying with friends or family; still others had decided to time repairs with larger renovation projects and weren't ready to be reconnected to the system.

---

41   Data retrieved from the Daily Briefing documents housed on the City of Lawrence Website in the Document Center under Gas Emergency: https://www.cityoflawrence. com/DocumentCenter/View/4836/20181025_Thursday-Daily-Brief_vF and https://www.cityoflawrence.com/DocumentCenter/View/4703/20181126_ Monday-Brief_vF and https://www.cityoflawrence.com/DocumentCenter/ View/4868/2018-12-03-Monday-Briefing-PDF.

But because of the CRO's final push to relight the remaining customers, on December 12, 2018, the Merrimack Valley restoration team declared that the project was "substantially complete."[42] This announcement was made with little to no fanfare. And, indeed, the project was not over. The company had committed to staffing the Lawrence operations center through the next year and to coming back to replace all the appliances that had been repaired during Operation Rapid Relight.

Columbia Gas, State and Local Officials Announce Gas Restoration Project 'Substantially Complete'

NEWS PROVIDED BY
Columbia Gas of Massachusetts →
12 Dec, 2018, 13:00 ET

SHARE THIS ARTICLE

LAWRENCE, Mass., Dec. 12, 2018 /PRNewswire/ -- Columbia Gas of Massachusetts and state and local officials today announced that restoration of gas service to residences and businesses in the Merrimack Valley is substantially complete.

With natural gas service restored to 98 percent of residential and business customers, the project has reached a major milestone and is in the process of entering the next phase of the restoration effort.

"Substantially complete" means that nearly all residences and businesses have heat, hot water and working gas appliances. There are less than 200 remaining customers who decided to "self-mitigate," or complete necessary assessments and installations themselves on their own timeline, independent of Columbia Gas contractors, or customers who have extenuating circumstances. Columbia Gas continues to offer its services to these customers should they request it. For the past two weeks, the team has been largely focused on supporting self-mitigators and customers with complex issues, and has invited all remaining customers with outage issues to contact Columbia Gas contractors to facilitate work before contractor resources ramp down.

A new chief operating officer of Merrimack Valley Operations for Columbia Gas of Massachusetts had been named—a veteran company leader who had spent September through December on the ground supporting the restoration work as part of the leadership team, and who

---

42   "Columbia Gas, State and Local Officials Announce Gas Restoration Project 'Substantially Complete.'" Columbia Gas of Massachusetts, 12 Dec. 2018, https://www.prnewswire.com/news-releases/columbia-gas-state-and-local-officials-announce-gas-restoration-project-substantially-complete-300764445.html. Press release.

had the background and the backbone to continue leading the effort for NiSource and Columbia Gas.

By the December 17 daily briefing session with the municipalities, over 98 percent of residential customers had been restored and only 92 self-migrating properties remained. Over 98 percent of business service had been restored with only 10 self-mitigating business customers remaining. The RV parks had been completely demobilized, and the company was working to facilitate the departure of the remaining families in hotel rooms and temporary apartments. Over $77 million in claims had been paid out to affected residents in the Merrimack Valley, and over 18,000 claims had been closed.[43]

On December 15, most of the day-to-day project leadership had exited the command center. A small group of people remained on the ground in the Merrimack Valley, but the remainder of employees, contractors and consultants wrapped up their duties, or were—if still assigned to the project—remotely attending the daily briefings for the rest of the year.

A few of us were assigned to Phase 2 of the Merrimack Valley Restoration Project, and those of us who were coming back to Lawrence tried to take some time off before hitting the ground running on January 2, 2019. But the crisis didn't just end. A few of the end-of-year developments included a large customer outage in Brockton, Massachusetts, during sub-zero temperatures. Although this was wholly unrelated to the events in the Merrimack Valley, any type of natural gas incident, especially involving Columbia Gas of Massachusetts, came under intense scrutiny and involved a much more robust response than would have been required prior to September 13.

Another obstacle encountered was a concern involving a small number of appliances installed during the restoration project at a local housing authority

---

43   Data retrieved from the Daily Briefing documents housed on the City of Lawrence Website in the Document Center under Gas Emergency: https://www.cityoflawrence. com/DocumentCenter/View/5023/2018-12-18--Monday-Briefing-PDF

apartment. Elevated levels of carbon monoxide were recorded in units where a certain model of stove had been installed. While the company addressed the issue by disconnecting the stoves and made the situation safe immediately, ultimately all of those appliances needed to be immediately replaced.

A third challenge that occurred before the end of the year involved the billing process and the issuance of natural gas bills to customers who may have had their service interrupted for a brief period of time immediately following the September 13 incident. These were not the affected customers whose natural gas lines were overpressurized, but rather customers who had either turned off their own gas service on September 13, or whose gas service was interrupted out of an abundance of caution. The company halted the billing process of every customer who had a service disruption following September 13, and those customers classified as "affected customers" were not charged for any gas service following the events in September. Those customers whose service was quickly restored, while not receiving a bill during the majority of the fourth quarter of 2018, began receiving bills for gas usage and service in late December or early January. With the focus on the restoration of service, the company neglected to inform these customers that bills would begin arriving for prior usage of natural gas. While the company offered payment plans and assistance to these customers, it put the team back on the defensive, and communication with our customers was once again called into question.

Despite the late-breaking challenges, the first phase of the crisis was officially resolved, with the majority of residents safely back at home with gas service restored and most businesses open to the public. But life would never be completely the same for residents of the Merrimack Valley. Some residents moved out of the area, and others, because of landlord-tenant issues needed to find other places to live. Residents whose homes were destroyed in the initial event on September 13 faced the difficult decision of whether to rebuild or relocate. And some businesses were not able to reopen due to the loss of revenue, which in turn affected residents who were employed by those businesses. Other businesses reopened only to close again because they just couldn't quite attract enough business after having been closed for an extended length of time.

It was a bittersweet ending for the Columbia Gas employees who had supported the effort as well. For those of us who had given so much of our time and energy to helping the residents of the Merrimack Valley and attempting to help the company restore its reputation, there was a lack of finality related to the situation. After working countless 16-hour days, and enduring intense questioning and criticism—after living through the highs of success and the lows of failure—most of the employees simply faded away, returning to their previous jobs with challenges that seemed irrelevant and petty by comparison. It was a difficult transition that was challenging for many.

With that said, having spent long weeks away from my family on the ground in Lawrence and having endured my own difficult transitions following the events in the Merrimack Valley, I was honored to have had the opportunity to help the residents in Massachusetts. I will remain forever grateful for the amazing friendships that came out of my experience, as well as the professional development and the intense crash course in crisis communications, the likes of which I had never seen before. And forever in my thoughts will be the residents of the Merrimack Valley, many of whom will live with those terrifying memories and trauma for the rest of their lives.

KEY TAKEAWAYS

(Lessons Learned)

No End in Sight: A crisis never really "ends." Even in a crisis situation that does not extend for months, events tend to linger following the initial response. As a member of the communications team, you will need to remain engaged in the situation and have an understanding and awareness of the events that continue after the initial public response. It is important to note that secondary situations can arise from the original crisis situation, and if lawsuits or other legal proceedings or investigations stem from the original event, each of those developments must be monitored closely. In the case of the Merrimack Valley, while the communications team in Phase 2 was much smaller, we retained people who were familiar with the Phase 1 work, and who understood the unique personalities of the communities, as well as the new project leadership. As you navigate your own crisis situations, it is helpful to think a few steps ahead and identify those individuals who will continue the work once the initial crisis quiets.

Feeding the Beast: Beware of secondary situations that may feed the original crisis. These secondary situations go beyond distractions and require their own crisis communications efforts. The billing situation in the Merrimack Valley is a great example of an indirect situation that renewed negative attention and reminded the area of the initial events in September, just as the situation was beginning to feel somewhat resolved. While it's imperative that you keep your focus on the mission at hand, it's also important to keep your ears open for other situations that may occur, and begin to consider a plan for those later developments.

Reputation Repercussions: Reputation management is not confined to only the area of the crisis itself. Other areas of your organization will feel the effects. In the case of a geographic crisis, such as the Merrimack Valley, the reputation risks extended far beyond that area. When dealing with a natural gas outage in Brockton, we were reminded of this. And in other states with Columbia Gas subsidiary companies, the events of the Merrimack Valley followed them as well. Even though the national coverage quickly waned after the events of September 13, a quick Google search by a reporter can turn up hundreds of articles pertaining to the situation. It's easy to make connections to crises—even ones that happened years ago. So, it's important to consider this in the case of your own crisis situations, and prepare for references and mentions to situations that may have preceded you as an employee.

Recognize Your Contributions: While crisis communications is not an easy field—many tears were shed in the Merrimack Valley by people responding to the crisis—remember that it is a privilege to work in this space. Yes, the hours are long, and the work is intense, but the opportunity to help either the company or the customers, and in some cases, both, is invaluable. It sharpens your skills, builds your network, and makes you a better communicator. Appreciate the chance to do work that makes an immediate difference, and learn from it. There is no better experience than real-time and real-life experience.

CHAPTER 16

NEXT STEPS AND FINAL WORDS ON THE MERRIMACK VALLEY CRISIS

A fter the events of September 13, NiSource and its Columbia Gas companies immediately put in place steps additional steps to enhance system safety and reliability and to safeguard against overpressurization.

The company committed to installing overpressurization protection devices on all low-pressure systems. These devices are meant to sense if natural gas operating pressure is too high or too low, and immediately and automatically shut down gas to the system. As a part of this program, the company also committed to installing remote monitoring devices on all low-pressure systems, so that its gas control centers have the ability to monitor pressure at regulator stations 24 hours a day, seven days a week.

Field surveys of all low-pressure regulator stations were conducted, and an engineering review of those regulator stations was put in place, while verifying and enhancing maps and records of low-pressure regulator stations. Additionally, NiSource implemented a requirement that company personnel be present whenever excavation work is being done in proximity to a regulator station, and engaged a third-party professional engineering firm to provide certification on all construction work packets.[44]

In addition to these steps, the company accelerated the implementation of a Safety Management System (SMS) across its operating footprint, in line with American Petroleum Institute (API) Recommended Practice (RP) 1173. The SMS process is meant to proactively identify and mitigate risk, and enhance its pipeline safety performance. As a part of the implementation of a SMS, the company also put into place a Quality Review Board (QRB) made up of safety industry experts to provide independent review and oversight over SMS work stream products, results, priorities and actions. The QRB comprises experts with diverse backgrounds spanning the nuclear, aviation and energy industries.

The company also developed an Emergency Preparedness and Response organization and deployed companywide training to any employee who may be involved in crisis response at the local or company level.

Despite all of these corrective actions, NiSource and Columbia Gas of Massachusetts faced multiple state and federal investigations, and in October of 2020, the Massachusetts DPU approved a $56 million settlement. The settlement would be used to provide debt relief to low-income natural gas customers and fund clean energy efficiency measures in older homes and

---

44 https://www.prnewswire.com/news-releases/nisource-statement-in-response-to-ntsb-safety-recommendation-report-300751805.html.

buildings. Subject to provisions in agreements with each the federal government and the state, NiSource and Columbia Gas of Massachusetts agreed to cease operations in Massachusetts and to sell its gas distribution business to Eversource Energy, which was completed on October 9, 2020.

Separately, the company paid a $143 million settlement stemming from a class-action lawsuit and a $53 million federal fine.

The events in the Merrimack Valley had widespread impact on the natural gas industry as well as on NiSource and Columbia Gas of Massachusetts. In April 2019, Massachusetts Senators Ed Markey and Elizabeth Warren and Congresswoman Lori Trahan introduced the Leonel Rondon Pipeline Safety Act, which was included in the passage of the PIPES Act (S. 2299) in August 2020. The legislation to reauthorize the Pipeline and Hazardous Materials Safety Administration (PHMSA) includes provisions drafted in response to the events in the Merrimack Valley, Massachusetts on September 13, 2018. Much of the legislation is drafted from the final NTSB report,[45] the recommendations of which will likely be required to be adopted by all natural gas distribution companies.

By implementing the NTSB's recommendations quickly and decisively, NiSource is now a safer company than it was in 2018, and that journey continues. In September of 2022, NiSource was recognized by LQRA, a leading global provider of professional engineering and technology services, for achieving conformance certification in API 1173 for its Safety Management System.[46] As of this writing, NiSource is only the second energy provider in the world to accomplish this safety goal. While the achievement is an important milestone in the company's safety journey, the company recognizes the need for continuous improvement. NiSource will continue to invest in its

---

45   https://www.ntsb.gov/investigations/AccidentReports/Reports/PAR1902.pdf

46   https://www.nisource.com/news/article/nisource-recognized-for-implementing-industry-leading-safety-management-system-20220922.

SMS and drive operational improvement and excellence through employee feedback, regular reviews, assessment of progress, identification of opportunities for improvement and transparent communications.

FINAL KEY TAKEAWAYS

(Lessons Learned)

Help Is Available: While multiple key takeaways have been presented throughout this case study, I will leave you with a few concluding thoughts. Each crisis is unique, and while you can prepare by reading texts and creating crisis communications plans, drafting and obtaining pre-approval for key statements, and understanding who will be on a "go-team" in the event of a large-scale crisis, you will never be able to fully prepare for the nuances of your particular event.

One important safety element that could have better prepared us for the events of September 13 and the months that followed may have been a more robust understanding and immediate implementation of the Federal Emergency Management Agency's (FEMA) Incident Command System (ICS) structure.[47] The ICS is a standardized hierarchical structure that allows for a cooperative response by multiple agencies, both within and outside of government, to organize and coordinate response activities without compromising the decision-making authority of local command. The role of ICS is

---

47 Columbia Gas of Massachusetts had an emergency management plan in place prior to the events of September 13, and the emergency plan was implemented on September 13; however, the plan was not sufficient given the magnitude of the disaster.

to establish planning and management functions to allow responding partners to take a coordinated and systematic approach. It includes assigning one central coordinator—the incident commander—to manage response activities by assigning personnel, deploying equipment, obtaining additional resources, and coordinating with participating partners as needed. The incident commander delegates emergency management responsibilities as needed, and thereby maintains the necessary focus on the overall picture of the disaster situation. The incident commander then assigns a series of functions such as Public Information Officer, Legal Officer, Safety Officer, along with a series of Section Chiefs to assume responsibility for all areas of crisis response.

The ICS is flexible and scalable, and had our company implemented or trained employees on this structure prior to September 13, the response to the unfolding crisis would have been faster and more efficient. Through the National Incident Management System (NIMS), FEMA offers a number of comprehensive and free trainings[48] available to anyone willing to take the time to complete the courses. While the training is intensive and time-consuming, I highly recommend that any communications professional invests the time and energy in completing the course. Even if your company sells a commercial product and is unlikely to interface with government agencies and emergency response personnel, or deal with a large-scale crisis, the training is worthwhile, and the structure can be adapted for any organization and any type of crisis. A standardized terminology and organizational structure may also be helpful to any type of business dealing with a wide range of crises.

---

48   https://training.fema.gov/nims/

Do Your Homework: While this is just one example of a crisis situation, plenty of case studies can be found by performing a quick internet search. Additionally, countless articles, checklists, planning templates, and statement examples are also available. Some of these materials are available on my website: www.thefourscoreteam.com. These valuable tools can be adapted to your organization. It may also be beneficial to take a look at some companies and consultants who can walk you through this process and help you to develop a crisis communication playbook specifically designed for your company. While there may be an expense associated with this type of work, when compared to the amount of money that a crisis could potentially cost your company, the investment will look small, indeed. Columbia Gas of Massachusetts ended up paying well over $1 billion due to the events of September 13, and with the inevitable increase in safety regulations that will be implemented for the entire industry as a result of the incident, the cost will continue to increase. Maybe having a strong crisis communications plan wouldn't have stopped the incident from happening, and it may not have prevented the severity of financial impact because of the incident, but perhaps it could have salvaged just a bit of the company's reputation in the state. And there's no telling how much money, time and frustration it could have saved in the end.

Lean into Action and then Reflect: In a crisis with a spotlight as bright as the Merrimack Valley natural gas accident, acting in any capacity can cause you to second-guess your decisions and question your role and contributions. Responding to *any* crisis is not easy. From the pace to the pressure to the perception to the prominence, the role of a communicator or public information officer comes with its own set of unique challenges. As you make quick decisions and act decisively, give yourself the grace to miss the mark at times. But rest in the knowledge that you know your work, colleagues and industry better than anyone else. And not even the most experienced crisis communicators have the answers to every crisis situation. The only way you become "good" at crisis communications is to go through a crisis (or two, or three, or more). There were many times I had to talk myself off the edge of imposter syndrome, the brink of self-flagellation, the precipice that I was assuredly not good enough. Looking back, it's easy to see that the best way to the end of the crisis is *through* the crisis, with a focus on the mission. Sometimes I had to be my own biggest advocate, at least in my mind. Having gone through it, I can now be your advocate. If you've read this text, you know more than I did when I stepped out of my rental car at the command center on Marston Street in the city of Lawrence for the first time. I figured it out. And so will you.

INDEX OF KEY TAKEAWAYS

Be Ready to Act: At least one member of your executive leadership team should be able to mobilize quickly and be prepared to make an on-camera statement in the event of a large-scale crisis. *Page 14.*

Understand Roles and Responsibilities: The role of the executive in front of the camera is different than the role of spokesperson in a large crisis situation where injuries, death and/or property damage has occurred. *Page 14.*

Establish External Relationships: Prior to a crisis, take some time to get to know your local media contacts by promoting stories of good will, if possible. *Page 15.*

Clarify Responsibility for Crisis Communications *Before* a Crisis: In companies with corporate communications departments as well as division communications teams, don't wait until an emergency to understand who is responsible for the communications function. *Page 15.*

Be Mindful of What's Important: At the end of the day, a company's reputation is built on how it treats its employees, its customers/stakeholders and the respect it shows the general public. *Page 16.*

CHAPTER 3
What's Going On?
Review Your Messaging and Read for Intent: To the extent that you can, as a communicator, partner with and guide your executives in their public statements and ensure that every word is both written and delivered with the proper intent. *Page 22.*

Take Responsibility: An apology and an acknowledgement of responsibility goes a long way. *Page 22.*

Practice Makes Perfect: It is worthwhile for your company to consider worst-case scenarios, draft a statement of apology and practice this statement during media training. *Page 23.*

Trust but Verify: Ensure that you and your team have factual and confirmed information to share. *Page 23.*

Understand Dependencies: Connections are key, both internally and externally. *Page 24.*

It's All Connected: For all companies, it is imperative that your leadership team spend time thinking about the interconnectivity of the various job functions of each department and the dependencies that exist between them. *Page 25.*

Don't Forget Your Co-workers: While internal communication is not the top priority in a situation as large as this one, consider assigning someone from your communications team to deliver messaging to the rest of the company through email, or the company intranet or web portal. *Page 25.*

CHAPTER 4
One Size Does Not Fit All
The Path to Intelligent Response: No matter your industry, company or discipline, before a crisis hits, know the demographic makeup of your customers or affected population. *Page 32.*

Method of Message Delivery: Take the time to understand how your customers would like to receive their information. *Page 32.*

Access to Messaging: These days, we tend to think largely in terms of technological delivery of messaging, but in some economically disadvantaged areas of the country, many residents don't have the same access to that technology. *Page 32.*

Personal Communications: Get out into the community (or reach out electronically) and talk to residents as quickly as possible after a crisis occurs to assess their needs. *Page 33.*

CHAPTER 5
And the Tide Started to Turn
Do the Right Thing: Stepping up and taking ownership of corporate social responsibility is extremely important in crisis situations. *Page 39.*

Rebuild the Bridge: If you do find yourself in a situation during which an attempt to make up for a lack of response or to regain control after a PR stumble is made, continued efforts to repair relationships with key stakeholders will begin to pay off. *Page 39.*

Continuous Learning Is Key: Focusing attention on areas that need improvement during a crisis should be a goal of every team member. Bringing on experts who are experienced with nuanced areas of response will allow you the ability to be agile and pivot quickly in all areas of crisis response (including communications). *Page 40.*

CHAPTER 6
Leadership Matters

A Single Source: During a crisis that the responsible communications person or team must have *one* identified source from which to receive updates and information; otherwise, the team will struggle to not only obtain information, but to obtain consistent and clear information. *Page 48.*

The Right Source: It is imperative during a crisis that the *right* person be placed in a position of authority. As a communicator, if you aren't getting the clear and consistent messaging you need, you certainly have the ability and the obligation to report any difficulties up the chain of command. *Page 49.*

Face It: Someone must be the "face" of the situation. The role of communications is to ensure the public and/or identified stakeholders receive the correct updates and the information they need. The job of communicator, unless explicitly identified, is not to take ownership of the situation itself or to present himself or herself as the face of the company. *Page 49.*

Listen to the People Who Matter: One theme that remains throughout any discussion of this event is the need to accept input from local communities. *Page 50.*

Work Toward the Same Goal: The need for coordination across departments is important, but coordination amongst the communications team during a crisis is just as critical. *Page 50.*

CHAPTER 7
The Plan Goes Public While the Crisis Continues
Modify Your Structure as Needed: The creation of the position of zone commander was arguably one of the greatest successes of the restoration effort itself, with the commanders acting in leadership roles both across their communities and internally, reporting out daily issues and situations that needed to be immediately addressed by the restoration leadership team. *Page 59.*

Keep It Simple: Make the communications materials as simple and as understandable as possible for your audience. *Page 60.*

Say Something: As a communicator, if you see the function suffering, speak up. *Page 61.*

Take Ownership: Consultants can be a great supplement to your team, but at the end of the day, it's the *company's* reputation that is on the line, not the consultant's reputation. *Page 61.*

Take Personal Chances: This is more of a personal word of advice rather than advice centered on communications, but when an opportunity to lead is presented to you, take it. *Page 62.*

CHAPTER 8
Political and Personal Motivations
Step Back: Communications is never a standalone function, but in a crisis situation, it is imperative that a holistic view of every aspect of communications is considered in order to adequately plan for every possible scenario. *Page 67.*

Consider Other Players: In any situation where Communications is asked to support, a stakeholder analysis is necessary. *Page 67.*

Know Your Team, and Structure Accordingly: Prepare before a crisis situation. Observe and understand the skills of the communicators on your team, or on other teams across your organization, assess where development needs to occur and invest in training courses where necessary. *Page 67.*

Filling the Gaps: Understand and plan where consultants and experts are necessary and can be incorporated into a situation when extra support is needed. *Page 68.*

CHAPTER 9
It's All Social
A Major Social Element: Be prepared for social media to become a key factor in your crisis communications response. *Page 76.*

It's Not All Bad: Although the threat of a post or a story going viral can cause fear even in the most seasoned of company leaders, social media has some tremendous benefits, including the ability to immediately gauge the impact of a story on branding or reputation, as well as providing an opportunity to quickly discern the public call to action. *Page 77.*

Put the Shoe on the Other Foot: Put yourself in your customers' position and communicate transparently and compassionately. *Page 77.*

It Can Get Noisy: Don't lose sight of your mission because of social media distractions. *Page 78.*

Follow the Rules: Ensure that employees know and understand your social media policies. And if you don't have policies regarding social media interaction, take the time to develop them. *Page 78.*

A Strategy That Lives On: Pay attention to your social media strategy throughout the life of the crisis. *Page 78.*

CHAPTER 10
Expect the Unexpected

The Crisis within a Crisis: Every challenge the team encountered required a full-scale communications plan, including internal communications (web updates and legal and executive interface), public relations mitigation, external affairs and community outreach, targeted customer communications and, in some cases, advertising opportunities to reach the largest audience. *Page 89.*

Get Out of Your Lane: In a large crisis situation, expect to veer far outside of your normal lane of operation. In normal business operations, communications teams may be included as a part of the process, but a communications professional will not typically be asked to make business decisions. In a crisis, many times, communication *is* the business decision. *Page 90.*

Managing Complexity: In situations involving intricate legal matters, try to set up a manageable review cycle ahead of time. *Page 90.*

Develop a Thick Skin: Communications is often the end of the line, and while as a communicator you may not have overall responsibility for the entire project, when things go wrong, "communication" will often be cited as the reason. *Page 91.*

CHAPTER 11
A Victory and a Major Setback
Transparency is Always the Right Decision... even if people don't like what you have to say. *Page 97.*

Keep it in Perspective: While it's critical to be flexible in the face of changing conditions, it also helps to keep in mind a constant and tangible objective to ground you in the face of upheavals and changes. *Page 98.*

The Value of a Public Forum: Town hall meetings, or other public forums, for information sharing are effective venues for engaging with the public. *Page 99.*

Take Good News Where You Can Get It: Even when positive news is overshadowed by unwelcome challenges or setbacks, it's still important to communicate (and celebrate) progress where you can. *Page 100.*

Consistency Is Key: The communications team is (or should be) involved in every aspect of a crisis. From speechwriting, talking points and town hall planning and execution, to social media updates, to website content, press releases and follow-up statements, it is imperative that the messaging is consistent. *Page 100.*

CHAPTER 12
Operation Deep Freeze
The Art of Preparing for the Worst-Case Scenario: No matter what secondary situations occur during a crisis, while the events may be outside of your control, the response is completely within your control. *Page 105.*

All for One, and One for All: While understanding roles and responsibilities is important, members of the team should also be prepared to pitch in wherever necessary to get the job done. *Page 105.*

CHAPTER 13
Happy Holidays
Extra Effort When It Matters Most: If going above and beyond is going to ease the suffering of the affected audience, consider the extra time, cost and resources as an investment in the well-being of your customers. *Page 110.*

Making Good News: In any crisis, the media has its own motivations. If you can create goodwill (without being insincere or manipulative, and for the good of the people and the cause) and entice the media to report it, this may help you repair a damaged reputation. *Page 111.*

Do Good Anyway: Even when intentions are good, members of the community may not always agree with a company's community involvement. Do good anyway. *Page 111.*

The Bright Spots: In a situation filled with angst, anger, frustration and turmoil, find some reasons to celebrate deeper meanings and relationships. *Page 112.*

CHAPTER 14
Dealing with Ancillary Issues
Keep Your Eye on the Ball: Distractions will inevitably be introduced into a crisis situation. At times, those distractions may be directly related to the crisis itself. But the distractions do nothing to change the mission at hand. React accordingly. *Page 117.*

Beware the Shadow of the Subplot: While, in many cases, a response to media inquiries related to distractions is required, social media will take on a life of its own. *Page 118.*

Coordination with Leaders: Ensure that your senior leadership understands and supports your strategy for dealing with ancillary and distracting developments or stories. *Page 119.*

Keep the Mission in Mind: External parties will have their own personal or professional motivations for reporting on, or even exploiting, a crisis. Stay focused on resolving the issue at hand and keeping the purpose of the mission top of mind. *Page 119.*

CHAPTER 15
A Rush to the Finish Line Where No One Was Cheering

No End in Sight: A crisis never really "ends." Events tend to linger following the initial response. As a member of the communications team, you will need to remain engaged in the situation and have an understanding and awareness of the events that continue after the initial public response. *Page 126.*

Feeding the Beast: Beware of secondary situations that may feed the original crisis. These secondary situations go beyond distractions and require their own crisis communications efforts. *Page 127.*

Reputation Repercussions: Reputation management is not confined to only the area of the crisis itself. Other areas of your organization will feel the effects. *Page 127.*

Recognize Your Contributions: While crisis communications is not an easy field, there is no better way to learn and no better experience than real-time and real-life experience. *Page 128.*

CHAPTER 16
Next Steps and Final Words on the Merrimack Valley Crisis

Help Is Available: If one thing could have prepared us, at least more than we were, for the events of September 13 and the months that followed, it would have been an understanding and immediate implementation of the Federal Emergency Management Agency's (FEMA) Incident Command System (ICS) structure. *Page 132.*

Do Your Homework: Many case studies, consultants and other crisis planning resources can be found by performing a quick internet search. Additionally, countless articles, checklists, planning templates, and statement examples are also available at no cost online. *Page 134.*

Lean into Action and then Reflect: From the pace to the pressure to the perception to the prominence, the role of a communicator or public information officer comes with its own set of unique challenges. As you make quick decisions and act decisively, give yourself the grace to miss the mark at times. But rest in the knowledge that you know your work, colleagues and industry better than anyone else. *Page 134.*

REFERENCES

1. National Transportation Safety Board (NTSB) Accident Report (2019). "Overpressurization of Natural Gas Distribution System, Explosions, and Fires in Merrimack Valley, Massachusetts September 13, 2018," https://www.ntsb.gov/investigations/AccidentReports/Reports/PAR1902.pdf.

2. Massachusetts Emergency Management Agency (2020). "Merrimack Valley Natural Gas Explosions After Action Report: September 13-December 16, 2018." https://www.mass.gov/doc/merrimack-valley-natural-gas-explosions-after-action-report/download.

3. Bombard, Noah R. "Columbia Gas Issues Statement Following Explosions in Lawrence, Andover and North Andover." 14 Sept. 2018. Retrieved from www.masslive.com/news/boston/2018/09/columbia_gas_issues_statement.html.

4. Bergstein, Brian. Bostonia (n.d.). "It was a suburban disaster: Questrom alum Joseph Albanese led a military recovery." Retrieved from https://www.bu.edu/articles/2019/merrimack-valley-gas-explosions-joe-albanese/.

5. Buell, Spencer. Boston Magazine. "As Frustration Mounts with Columbia Gas, Baker Declares a State of Emergency." Posted 14 Sept. 2018. Retrieved from https://www.bostonmagazine.com/news/2018/09/14/state-of-emergency-columbia-gas-fire-lawrence/. Accessed November 2020.

6. United States Senate, Office of Senator Ed Markey, Senator for Massachusetts. "Senators Markey and Warren Demand Answers About Merrimack Valley Gas Explosions and Fires," 17 Sept. 2018, https://www.markey.senate.gov/imo/media/doc/Letter%20to%20NiSource%20and%20Columbia%20Gas.pdf.

7. City of Lawrence. (n.d.). Lawrence gas emergency. Retrieved from https://www.cityoflawrence.com/718/Lawrence-Gas-Emergency.

8. City of Lawrence (n.d.) About the City. Retrieved from https://www.cityoflawrence.com/501/About-the-City.

9. "Lawrence, Massachusetts." *Wikipedia,* Wikimedia Foundation, 30 Nov. 2020, https://en.wikipedia.org/wiki/Lawrence,_Massachusetts.

10. "North Andover, Massachusetts." *Wikipedia,* Wikimedia Foundation, 5 Dec. 2020, https://en.wikipedia.org/wiki/North_Andover,_Massachusetts.

11. "Andover, Massachusetts." *Wikipedia,* Wikimedia Foundation, 30 Nov. 2020, https://en.wikipedia. org/wiki/Andover,_Massachusetts.

12. "Commodore Builders." (n.d.) *Joe Albanese,* Retrieved November 2022, from https://commodorebuilders.com/people/joseph-j-albanese/.

13. "Tiger Team." *Wikipedia,* Wikimedia Foundation, 31 May 2021, https://en.wikipedia.org/wiki/Tiger_team.

14. Federal Emergency Management Agency. "ICS Organizational Structure and Elements." Retrieved December 2020, from https://training.fema.gov/emiweb/is/icsresource/assets/ics%20organizational%20structure%20and%20elements.pdf.

15. U.S. Department of Energy, Office of Energy Policy and Systems Analysis. "Natural Gas Infrastructure Modernization Programs at Local Distribution Companies: Key Issues and Considerations," January 2017. https://www.energy.gov/sites/prod/files/2017/01/f34/Natural%20Gas%20Infrastructure%20Modernization%20Programs%20at%20Local%20Distribution%20Companies--Key%20Issues%20and%20Considerations.pdf.

16. Boston 25 News Facebook Page, accessed November 2020: https://www.facebook.com/watch/live /?v=329093114333088&ref=watch_permalink

17. Boston 25 News, "Timeline of events during Merrimack Valley gas explosions." Posted 18 Sept., 2018. Retrieved from https://www.boston25news.com/news/emergency-crews-responding-to-multiple-fires-following-explosions-in-lawrence/833085938/. Accessed November 2020.

18. @MassStatePolice. MSP Fusion Center has current updated tally of responses to fires/explosions/investigations of gas odor at 70. Spread over wide swath of south #Lawrence and northern part of #NorthAndover with several others across Merrimack River in north Lawrence. *Twitter,* 13 Sep. 2018, 7:25 pm, twitter.com/MassStatePolice/status/1040380980815687680?s=20&t=jtwe72kuiVOQr73aRXorKA.

19. WCVB Channel 5 Boston. "Evacuation order for Columbia Gas Customers. Call to Action to Share." Facebook, 13 Sep. 2018, 6:19 pm, https://www.facebook.com/wcvb5/posts/pfbid02k6YVR7mkbYeQWG6G3M9cz9J8niQP47V9UpDHeXZnYk2LG6QetLJcyJPBGb1jiCsUl.

20. @BostonGlobe. "We are sorry," said Steve Bryant, the president of Columbia Gas of Massachusetts on Friday after Thursday's explosions and fires, adding, "This is the sort of thing a gas distribution company hopes never happens." *Twitter,* 14 Sep. 2018, 5:41pm, twitter.com/BostonGlobe/status/1040717088644583425? s=20&t=3wvwzXuv7rVYrPfE3UTVoA.

21. @SenWarren. The people of Massachusetts deserve answers from @ColumbiaGasMA about how these tragic gas explosions happened. @MassGovernor and Lawrence Mayor @danrivera01843 have said Columbia isn't following through – I support the decision to have another company oversee recovery efforts. *Twitter,* 14 Sep. 2018, 8:33pm, https://twitter.com/SenWarren/status/1040760487452000257?s=20&t=jtwe72kuiVOQr73aRXorKA.

22. "Columbia Gas makes $10 million donation to the Greater Lawrence Disaster Relief Fund." Columbia Gas of Massachusetts, 18 Sep. 2018, www.prnewswire.com/news-releases/columbia-gas-makes-10-million-donation-to-the-greater-lawrence-disaster-relief-fund-300714733.html. Press release.

23. "Columbia Gas announces "gas ready" construction restoration plan for Greater Lawrence; nearly 200 construction crews working to restore gas service by November 19." Columbia Gas of Massachusetts, 2 Oct. 2018, https://www.prnewswire.com/news-releases/columbia-gas-announces-gas-ready-construction-restoration-plan-for-greater-lawrence-nearly-200-construction-crews-working-to-restore-gas-service-by-november-19-300722978.html. Press Release.

24. Harmacinski, Jill. The Eagle Tribune, 8 Oct. 2018. "Hotels fill, trailers arrive, shelter opens under gas housing plan." https://www.eagletribune.com/news/merrimack_valley/hotels-fill-trailers-arrive-shelter-opens-under-gas-housing-plan/article_7d310cdd-77d1-5371-ae90-fd38d0c11372.html.

25. "Columbia Gas Completes Gas Pipeline Construction Project, Now Fully Focused on In-Home Work." Columbia Gas of Massachusetts, 30 Oct. 2018, https://www.prnewswire.com/news-releases/columbia-gas-completes-gas-pipeline-construction-project-now-fully-focused-on-in-home-work-300740339.html. Press release.

26. "Columbia Gas Prepares Thanksgiving Dinner For Merrimack Valley Explosion Victims." WBZ News, CBS Boston, 21 Nov. 2018, https://www.cbsnews.com/boston/news/thanksgiving-merrimack-valley-explosions-columbia-gas/.

27. "Gas company facing federal criminal investigation after explosions, fires." WCVB5, 1 Nov. 2018, https://www.wcvb.com/article/gas-company-facing-federal-criminal-investigation-after-explosions-fires/24513587.

28. "NiSource Statement in Response to NTSB Safety Recommendation Report." NiSource, 15 Nov. 2018, https://www.prnewswire.com/news-releases/nisource-statement-in-response-to-ntsb-safety-recommendation-report-300751805.html. Press release.

29. Hensel, Karen. NBC10 Boston. "Whistleblower: Columbia Gas Cut Corners Prior to Explosions," 11 Dec. 2018, https://www.nbcboston.com/news/local/whistleblower-columbia-gas-cut-corners-prior-to-explosions/130040/.

30. Cooper, Steve. Associated Press. "'No second chances': Mass. politicians say Columbia Gas should close," WHDH, Boston, 26 Nov. 2018, https://whdh.com/news/no-second-chances-mass-politicians-say-columbia-gas-should-close/.

31. "Columbia Gas, State and Local Officials Announce Gas Restoration Project 'Substantially Complete.'" Columbia Gas of Massachusetts, 12 Dec. 2018, https://www.prnewswire.com/news-releases/columbia-gas-state-and-local-officials-announce-gas-restoration-project-substantially-complete-300764445.html. Press release.

32. "NiSource Statement in Response to NTSB Safety Recommendation Report." NiSource, Nov. 15, 2018, https://www.prnewswire.com/news-releases/nisource-statement-in-response-to-ntsb-safety-recommendation-report-300751805.html. Press release.

33. "NiSource recognized for implementing industry-leading Safety Management System." Sept. 22, 2022, https://www.nisource.com/news/article/nisource-recognized-for-implementing-industry-leading-safety-management-system-20220922. Press release.